HEALTH; AN INSIDE JOB AN OUTSIDE BUSINESS

Our State of Health is mainly governed by marketing, conditioned beliefs and misinformation

A supplemental handbook to The Business of Disease Documentary

Revised and Expanded Edition

Sonia Barrett

TIMELINE PUBLISHING INC.,
North Hollywood, CA

Contents

DEDICATION

This book is dedicated to all those who dare to leap into the unknown in search of self and to those who have paved the way through their research, through the sacrifice and through their unwavering trek into those dimly lit corners. Because of you there is light and inspiration in seeing just how deep the rabbit hole goes.
Thank you!

Foreword

When Sonia Barrett, producer, author, media expert, and the editor of *Health an Inside Job and Outside Business* asked me to be an interviewee in her documentary film, *The Business of Disease*, and then to write the foreword to this book, I was excited to join the conversation. To be riding on a wave that, in my opinion, is flowing from the heart of human care and combined global effort into the next evolution – the evolution of consciousness – is a deeply felt experience. Sonia has her finger on the pulse of a new era in which we will see tremendous leaps in the way we as whole living beings of body, mind, and spirit approach health, happiness, and meaningful living. And with that, I invite you all to join in.

The timing for this book (and its film) is ideal, given today's struggling system of healthcare. *Health an Inside Job and Outside Business* offers a new direction.

Consider this:

What if someone were to tell you that many if not most of the illness that you will encounter in your lifetime could be avoided naturally, without the need for drug treatment or invasive surgical or clinical action? What if someone were to tell you that the new revolution in medicine will focus on generating preventatives, curatives, and more natural remedies for maximum living, using the frequencies of your own mind and body? What if someone were to tell you that you could use your mind to alter genes and divert or eliminate specific human diseases? Or that the right fine art, body movement, or natural environmental influence could heal your chronic pain, stress, insomnia, depression, ADD/ADHD? Or that you can generate a brand new brain with new circuits for positive emotions?

Are these things possible? From the perspective of mind-body medicine, the answer is a resounding yes.

So the imminent questions are: What kind of brain do you want? What kind of mind? How do *you* want to live? And when do you want to start?

It seems wherever you go today you can hear stories of individuals dealing with irritating side-effects of pharmaceuticals or worse, of people who have (or know someone who has) experienced great catastrophe from regimented drug treatment. This is not to say that all drug treatment is bad for everyone, yet such incidents abound. Nonetheless, chemical treatment – here in our own country – whether it is to relieve pain or deal with other malaise, physical or mental, is the first choice of treatment. Many individuals concerned about their health unfortunately believe this is the way things "have to be." This is because most of us are conditioned to think this way from early childhood. By the time most of us are adults, we have bought into the idea. And this mentality is spreading worldwide.

We have all heard of situations in which an individual takes a mountain of prescription drugs to treat a particular disorder, yet nothing works and side-effects to the pharmaceuticals worsen. Long-term regimens may even require treating symptoms that arise from the first treatment. In so many of these stories, when conditions worsen and drug treatments are not working out, the next steps may become more invasive.

Sometimes we hear that an individual, having run the gamut and having little choice left, sees an alternative medical practitioner who, when there is still enough time to potentially make a difference, uses a more natural, no-side-effect approach and it works. But this should not be seen as some kind of universal outcome. Is such a result always the case? No. Do we know the reasons why certain methods work with one individual and not another? Just as with mainstream medicine, it seems the honest answer would be similar: "sometimes we do, but certainly not every time." More funding for research in this specific area would help shed some light here and hopefully lead to even greater precision. The more important truth, however, is that those methods can work.

We know too that mindfulness, an important component of holistic medicine across the world, is currently the rage in Western healthcare – so much so that it was the subject of a recent cover story in *Time* magazine. Yet, mindfulness has been a core element of holistic medicine for millennia. Traditional Chinese Medicine (TCM) alone has developed and advanced what we call *mindfulness* into a primary mind-body mechanism for health and well-being. Historically, they have documented their science (as it has progressed) on mindfulness sequentially in over 6,000 medical books, over many long years. The history and role of mindfulness in Ayurveda and Mind-Body medicine are similar. There is much to learn especially from these traditions who have experimented with both the science *and* enlightenment of mind-body connectivity for better physical, psychological, and spiritual (nondenominational) health, for thousands of years.

Leading the way, projects like *Health an Inside Job and Outside Business* and *The Business of Disease* are drilling down much deeper into mind-body-spirit consciousness and connectivity, and its possibilities are illuminating the path so many people are now demanding and seeking in whole being healthcare. The time is right and the time is now.

So I am optimistic and grateful to Sonia Barrett and all of the voices in *Health an Inside Job and Outside Business* for helping give greater visibility to the more in-depth ideas, techniques and profound capabilities of holistic medicine and healthcare.

In doing so, several of the authors in the following pages will share with you a story of their own personal battle with a serious healthcare issue. The common thread is that each was forced to break out of the box of conventional thinking in order to heal. You will travel with them in their quest for new science and a more enlightened learning and ultimately to their triumph over suffering. Their tools will then become your tools – if you choose.

What all of us in this book agree on is that cultivating a relationship between the mind and body is essential to the prevention and cure of disease, whether acute or chronic.

Each chapter offers a way to live more naturally and organically, being fully you and simultaneously part of something larger, which as we are discovering, more and more, plays a significant role in the healthy development of your whole living being.

One of the experts you will meet is naturopathic doctor, Romeo Brooks. Much like the rest of us, having witnessed firsthand in his own family what damage uncured disease can wield, he turned a major part of his life's work toward a search for better and quicker health solutions. Disease says Dr. Romeo is the action of the whole body. He urges readers, "Cultivate a relationship with your body. Develop your senses and awareness of its voice. It is making a request based on its needs. By quieting the mind, stopping the mental chatter and listening, you will learn to become more perceptive to your body's request."

Enter Bernando LaPallo who is 111 years young and does just that – listens in on his life. You will see how as he shares with you his secrets to vitality and age. Neuroscientist Dr. Katherine L. Rossi gives a compelling account of her own battle with chronic pain and how recovery became possible as she listened in on her body and mind. Her resolve is breathtaking, and you won't forget her passionate mantra, "If I can experience five minutes without pain," she says, "I can create a lifetime without pain." Her personal story is vividly told and beautifully victorious. But more than that, she teaches us how we too can alleviate or better yet ward off our own pain all together. She dramatically asks, "What type of brain do you want to create?" This question may give you pause – can you actually create a "new" brain? Yet, science tells us we can, and Dr. Rossi has done it and mapped her path as a tool for others to discover how you can use your own mind to do the same.

From the very first pages of this book, you will be filled with cutting-edge insights, inspiration, the truth of personal experience and new science and a growing feeling of self-empowerment. You will share in the excitement of scientific discovery and the triumphs of the mind over disease. You share with us in exercising the mind's capacity to create beauty and health and life.

You will want to try out the many activities and techniques discussed in each chapter. I know this because I did! And you can't help but want to give them a go right away. This is because in our most organic and honest core, they will ring true.

There are so many inspiring moments. I especially enjoyed Dr. Jacob Liberman's discussion of our mind-body's ultimate source of wisdom and healing, which according to Dr. Liberman, is as an expansive aspect of our nature; where self and divine are one. Your eyes, the windows of your soul, he says, will help you discover this unity – this oneness. On a personal note, I couldn't agree more.

"The eyes," he writes, "are not separate from the brain. They are extensions of the brain. Two satellite dishes that connect the outer worlds with our inner world ... Interestingly, whether our eyes are open or closed, when we focus on something, our eyes respond in exactly the same way."

From the point of view of mind-body medicine this is a mechanism to profound mindfulness, with science behind it. Combined with the notion and mechanism of consciousness, you now have an extremely powerful tool with which to transform your health and life.

So what kind of brain do you want? Your answer to this question will determine what kind of mind you cultivate and absolutely what kind and quality of whole being life you will have.

As such, *Health an Inside Job and Outside Business* is much about creation and choice.

Physicist, Dr. Amit Goswami uses quantum physics to explain the healing power of integral medicine. I was so glad to see and hear his voice within this collection. He poses another question, "Where is the discernible signature of [your] choice then?" Where is the seat of your power to create?

His answer joins ancient wisdom and physics, "In the psyche, inside our consciousness." But he points out, "you have to go through a process."

Health an Inside Job and Outside Business de-mystifies that very process and offers you the way in – starting today.

You will keep re-reading Dr. Goswami's detailed explanation of how to engage this creative process into your psyche – as with each time through you will enhance your skill and reap more meaningful and satisfying personal transformations.

Health an Inside Job and Outside Business throws away the old idea that we have just one healthcare choice and that it is mainstream medicine and provides many of us with what we have been long waiting for: Clarity and another choice.

The process of whole being living and healthcare is a riveting one. While you are reading this book you will experience many breakthrough moments. May its concepts and techniques serve you well.

Dr. Joseph Cardillo, PhD

Author of *The Five Seasons: Tap Into Nature's Secrets for Health, Happiness, and Harmony*

Introduction

We live in a time where our personal definition and expression of freedom is in question; although we may debate that freedom throughout history seem to have been defined by the times. Our world has been on an upswing in technology as we witness diverse extremes of power and control. Through gradualism many are guided into methods and ideologies that remove us from authenticity and from our ability to provide true self-care. How can self-care an innately natural response be relinquished to governing systems outside of us, causing us to forget that *"the cure is in the body, not in the business"* a phrase coined for The Business of Disease documentary. *Health; An Inside Job An Outside Business* is a rich source of insights contributed by those featured in the documentary produced by Sonia Barrett.

Health; An Inside Job an Outside Business, was created in support of the documentary. This book is in essence an extension of the film. The intent being that after reviewing the film the book will serve as support to those inspired by the film as they embark on a new journey of personal change. This book far exceeds words from a collection of professionals in their fields, but rather it shares the wisdom of minds passionate about self-discovery and personal freedom.

They bring to our attention the hypnosis of marketing, belief systems and the body's ability to heal. Not only do they shed light on the disinformation presented as health care but they have integrated science as a means of clarifying the possibilities which exists in better understanding the inner technology of spirit, mind and body. Through a holistic approach in dealing with dis-ease, options and insights are presented as readers are encouraged to examine the whole being. The marketing of dis-ease is examined along with the genetic and social programs from which our choices and experiences are shaped. We are encouraged to be unafraid to take responsibility for our bodies, our spirits and our minds.

Through this shared wisdom and insights they bridge the gap between science and spirituality in a way that truly brings to the forefront what is possible. These are voices of freedom for those ready to leap into a new level of inner freedom as external change begins with an inner revolution.

Ann Boroch, C.N.C, Naturopath, addresses our exposure to external influences which greatly affect our beliefs and fears; *"Advertising isn't helping matters. Television, radio, billboards, magazines and the internet bombard us with advertisements for pharmaceutical medications. After a while, we become fearful and begin to wonder if we don't have the many symptoms or conditions cited. These constant and repetitive advertisements instill fear and promote a dependency on a "quick fix" pill or drug. As a result, we have become a culture conditioned to expecting a "silver bullet" to cure all our ailments. There is no silver bullet."*

Dr. Romeo Brooks reminds us that; *"Simply put, disease is a struggle. It is a struggle that the body engages in on its own behalf. It is a struggle of intent and precision. No matter what it looks like, no matter what course of action the body takes, no matter how radical the symptoms may appear, its survival is at hand."* Through these pages the struggle in your own life becomes clear and perhaps providing you with insight into your own body's dis-ease.

Dr. Bradley Nelson takes us on a journey in understanding the impact of our emotions on our health; *"Removing trapped emotions can often relieve pain and suffering, even in cases that would be considered hopeless by conventional medicine."*

Sharry Edwards explains to us the complexity of the body's design and yet the simplicity of self-healing; *"Our bodies are animated through a complex network of nerves that serve as a communication matrix from our brain and spinal cord to every nook and cranny of our bodies. The neural system generates frequencies that move along these pathways. Any self-healing of the body must interact with these "bio-frequencies". Every aspect of this communication network reaches the brain as a measurable frequency; from sound, to thought, to aroma, to light, to touch.... Bottom line, the brain uses frequency to maintain and have dominion over our structure and function. "*

Dr. Amit Goswami raises a significant point in examining the manner in which we place tremendous focus outside of ourselves. We relentlessly attempt to fix everything and everyone outside of our self while we evade the needed changes within. *"People want others to change, but not themselves; that's the goal of usual activism. Quantum activism from the get go declares that doesn't work simply because the movement of consciousness is not designed to be like that; it is designed to further human evolution."*

Dr. Ernest Rossi clarifies the art of healing: *"We normally outgrow many symptoms of stress, trauma and post traumatic problems (PTSD). Further, we can actually learn to facilitate our own natural healing process of mind-gene communication by heightening our consciousness in everyday life with what I call "the Novelty-Numinosum-Neurogenesis Effect (NNNE)." A simple passive exposure to beauty and truth may not be enough, however. We need to deeply experience the genuine activity of creating new consciousness in everyday life by heightening our personal motivation to turn on our healing genes with the NNNE!"*

These amazingly diverse collections of insights allow readers to connect with information relevant to their personal situations. Each chapter is written completely from the heart and soul of the contributor. No one knew what the other wrote until it was all completed. As a result this life changing book was born.

As you move through these pages may you be inspired to find a deeper appreciation for your journey and for where you are at this moment in your life. Each and every moment is ripe with opportunities to discover an unyielding power within. May you experience true freedom as you move through the journey of health. Live unafraid and with passion, take chances and simply live! The direction of your journey lies with you!

CHAPTER 1

Dr. Romeo Brooks, PhD

The Nature of Disease

The body, because of its inherent intelligence, possesses above all things the intention, purpose and desire to maintain itself in balance and harmony. It is in our best interest to support this effort in the most natural way possible.

The purpose of this chapter is to disclose the true nature and purpose of disease, its root cause and varied manifestations. From time immemorial to present day, man has viewed disease and its processes within the human body as something illusive, mysterious and somewhat magical. It is no wonder that we continue to create so- called "cures" for something we do not understand.

We imagine that one day even a shot in the dark might hit the target. The problem with this approach is that you will never know when you hit the target because it is in the dark. As long as we look for the answer in the darkness, the answers that stand clearly in the bright and shining light of day will never be found. To remove the cause of disease would be the logical conclusion for anyone looking to eradicate the effects of disease. So what remains for us is to define the cause and eliminate it.

Sometimes it is necessary to say what a thing is not to better understand what it is. If we start with the wrong premise, we will end up with the wrong idea. It needs to be made clear and understood from the beginning that disease is not a noun. It is not a person, place, or thing. It is not an entity. It is not a condition. It is not your high blood pressure or diabetes, or asthma. Disease is not contagious and it does not cause epidemics. It is not an attack on your body by germs, viruses, bacteria, parasites, or fungus.

Disease is a verb. It is a word describing action. This action is caused by the body, generated by the body and controlled by the body. It is the energy of the body set in motion to cleanse, repair and restore itself. It is conducted by the body in response to the accumulated waste within its tissues.

Therefore, it is a compensatory act. It is the body's intelligence at work and it is always constructive. Webster's dictionary defines disease as "a condition of the living animal or plant or body or one of its parts that impairs the performance of a vital function." This is absolutely wrong. Disease is the vital function. The function is not one of impairment but one of repair to the body. Webster also defines it as "a harmful development." Disease is not a harmful development; it is a proper development. It is a development to make things better.

Simply put, disease is a struggle. It is a struggle that the body engages in on its own behalf. It is a struggle of intent and precision. No matter what it looks like, no matter what course of action the body takes, no matter how radical the symptoms may appear, its survival is at hand.

Disease is the body's way of detoxifying itself. This detoxification process may appear in the form of a seizure as in epilepsy, the shaking of Parkinson's or the simple cough of a cold. In all three cases the physiological response is the same: to expel, neutralize or compartmentalize poisons that have accumulated above the body's tolerance level.

When toxic accumulations rise above the body's tolerance level, it institutes disease(s) for the purposes of elimination. This is why when we are diseased, the whole body is diseased.

The body is not a group of fragmented systems, organs and glands that have been put together like an automobile. The body is one. The cardiovascular system cannot say to the respiratory system "I can breathe without you." Nor can the muscular system say to the skeletal system, "I can walk without you". What about the nervous system telling the digestive system, "I can eat without you"? This is absurd, yet this kind of thinking is taught in schools all over the world.

Disease is the action of the whole body detoxifying. It does not matter if the body's compensatory efforts are experienced in one particular area or another. Whether symptoms appear in the heart, liver, kidneys, lungs, brain, etc., it is still the action of the entire body unburdening itself.

What if you were on a jet ready for takeoff and the flight attendant announced that there was a bomb threat? If the passengers in their panic overcrowded one exit as opposed to the other, would you say that the only problem was the overcrowded exit? Absolutely not. Then, if the body chose to send waste out through every possible channel and the kidneys happen to get loaded beyond their capacity, is there something wrong with the kidneys only? When this action is displayed by the body, the name of the disease given is according to whatever organ or organs get overcrowded.

This is why my brother had fourteen different doctors. He had one for his heart, one for his diabetes, one for his blood pressure, one for his kidneys, etc. Specialists in their field of expertise have isolated diseases to fit into specific categories. To see any disease as singular and unrelated to the entire body would be myopic.

For example, what grade would you give a restaurant that had beautiful chandeliers, gorgeous paintings and a romantic atmosphere, but the kitchen and restrooms were rat and roach-infested? Would you say it was excellent except for the kitchen and restrooms? Of course not. The entire restaurant would be considered unfit and in need of extermination. Disease is a crisis of the entire body focusing its efforts on house cleaning.

You should be aware that the initial onset of any disease is considered to be acute. Acute disease is a healing mechanism and is self-limited; that is, it will end its course of action with healing. It is the body's way of uprooting and ejecting anything foreign that may have been implanted.

In acute diseases (colds, flu, fever), the body's signals are clear, but misunderstood by most. Our interpretation of them causes us to respond inappropriately. We simply want to pacify ourselves immediately, and as pleasurably as possible. However, when acute diseases have been suppressed with drugs or processed foodstuffs, the body's messages are muffled, leading to chronic disease.

Chronic disease can only occur when the body's initial efforts to uproot and eject this foreign matter have been halted or suppressed, causing this material to be buried, take root and cause tissue damage. In chronic disease the body is only adapting, not healing. When symptoms are forced underground, the body sacrifices parts of itself to maintain some semblance of balance.

Contrary to contemporary school of thought, chronic disease is not what causes death. It is the body's natural process of detoxification. The body still speaks to us through chronic disease by alerting us that the problem is still unresolved.

This is why a chronic disease must become an acute disease once again to effect a healing. The evolution from acute disease to chronic disease must be reversed. Therefore, it is in our best interest not to suppress acute or chronic disease with drugs or other pharmaceutical poisons. If medications are ingested, the body must divert its energy from the process of healing to focus on the new poison that has been introduced. When this happens the symptoms of disease disappear, giving the illusion of wellness, but the body's toxicity level is increased. This suppression and increase in toxicity is what causes an acute disease to become chronic. At this point we continue to attempt to resolve chronic disease with the same logic; that is, by adding more toxicity to an already toxic body. Somehow the insanity of this approach must be seen for what it is.

Cultivate a relationship with your body. Develop your senses and awareness of its voice. It is making a specific request based on its needs. By quieting the mind, stopping the mental chatter and listening, you will learn to become more perceptive to the body's request.

In order for us to reach our full potential and longevity, it is necessary that we place our confidence in the fact that the body is the only entity capable of building health. It is self-directing, self-constructing, self-defending, self-preserving, self-maintaining and, if injured or ill, self-repairing and self-healing.

No one has the authority or power to control bodily functions and do a better job than the body itself. Was the body designed by a pharmaceutical company, an elite group of doctors or some secret government agency? No, it was designed by God to cleanse, heal and repair itself. The only thing we can ever do is supply the body with its biological needs; otherwise, we will interfere with or hamper operations beyond our capacity to ascertain.

CHAPTER 2

Ann Boroch, C.N.C, Naturopath

Who Is Your Best Healthcare Provider—You Are!

Americans are getting sicker by the minute. Today, 1 out of 3 people have cancer or type 2 diabetes; 1 out of 12 have an autoimmune disease; 1 in 8 elderly have Alzheimer's; and 1 out of 88 American children have autism.

Why are we so sick? Because we are toxic. We breathe polluted air, eat denatured food, drink contaminated water, overuse or abuse pharmaceutical medication, and cannot or do not manage our stress. Food producers and chemical companies are flooding the market with products that are dangerous to our health. Rather than focusing on education and prevention, our medical system focuses almost exclusively on crisis management and pushes pharmaceutical drugs and surgeries instead.

Advertising isn't helping matters. Television, radio, billboards, magazines and the internet bombard us with advertisements for pharmaceutical medications. After a while, we become fearful and begin to wonder if we don't have the many symptoms or conditions cited. These constant and repetitive advertisements instill fear and promote a dependency on a "quick fix" pill or drug. As a result, we have become a culture conditioned to expecting a "silver bullet" to cure all our ailments. There is no silver bullet.

Companies make foods convenient, tasty and cheap, but these foods are full of chemicals and devoid of nutrients. Grocery stores are stocked with processed foods filled with sugars, trans fats, refined flours, and preservatives that inflame your body.

Faced with this reality, it is easy to feel overwhelmed and powerless. But the truth is that you are in the driver's seat and in control of your health. We must not forget that the body has an innate intelligence—an ability to repair itself and maintain balance. Supporting your body's intelligence is the key to getting better.

The first step is to make the choice to be healthy. Second, educate yourself on nutrition and health. Last, take action and be diligent in making better lifestyle choices.

WHAT ARE THE ROOT CAUSES THAT BREAK A BODY DOWN?

Inflammation is the main cause of disease and is attributable to four factors. The first factor is infection, which is brought on by candida, fungus, parasites, bacteria, and/or viruses. Second are environmental toxins, such as petrochemicals, pesticides, herbicides and heavy metals. Third is nutritional deficiency and toxicity in the body. Fourth is unmanaged stress. The ratios will vary for each person but the longer these conditions go unaddressed, the more inflammation builds and the more symptomatic you become. Eventually, conditions such as diabetes, chronic pain, Alzheimer's, cancer, autoimmune illnesses and cardiovascular diseases can develop.

Candida Overgrowth—The Missing Link

The most grossly ignored infection in the world is candida overgrowth. Candida is yeast and fungus. What is yeast? It is a ubiquitous single-celled organism that naturally lives everywhere inside and outside the body, and stays balanced until we upset that balance. The common disruptors of this balance are antibiotics, steroids, birth control pills, hormone replacement, chemotherapy, radiation, vaccinations, heavy metals, stress, sugar and alcohol. You only need one dose of antibiotics in your lifetime to begin a vicious cycle of yeast overgrowth and infection.

Here's how it works. Let's say you are seven years old and you have an ear infection. The doctor gives you antibiotics. The antibiotics wipe out both good and bad bacteria in the gastrointestinal tract because they cannot distinguish between the two. Without enough good bacteria, candida (yeast) begins to multiply. Yeast produces 79 toxic by-products (mycotoxins), which weaken your immune system, causing you to fall ill again with the same recurring infection or a new one in a different part of your body. The doctor gives you more antibiotics, which wipe out more good bacteria, continuing to weaken your immune system even more. Eventually yeast turns into fungus (mycelia root forms) that burrows and pokes holes in the intestinal lining, known as leaky gut. The fungus and mycotoxins migrate into the bloodstream, disrupting communication in the body and attacking tissues and organs. So what begins as harmless yeast ultimately becomes pathogenic fungus.

Among those causes of candida overgrowth identified above, sugar is the biggest offender, and is the food that will continue to feed yeast and fungus throughout a lifetime. Sugar means cookies, chocolate, pizza, pasta, pastries, lattes, milk, cheese, wine, beer, and bread—all of which turn into sugar rapidly and feed not only yeast, but parasites, viruses and bacteria.

Minor symptoms of candida overgrowth can be gas, bloating, heartburn, fatigue, weight gain, depression, anxiety, sinusitis, constipation and diarrhea. More serious conditions are autoimmune diseases and cancer. See Figure 1 to learn how the body's systems are affected by yeast overgrowth.

Environmental Toxins

The second factor making us sick today is environmental toxins from pesticides, herbicides, fungicides, xenoestrogens (petroleum-based chemicals that have estrogen-like effects in the body), cigarettes, pharmaceutical medications, heavy metals (lead, cadmium, mercury) and vaccinations.

More than ever before we are being exposed to massive amounts of chemicals in our food, air and water supply. Unfortunately, government agencies such as the Federal Drug Administration (FDA), American Medical Association, American Dental Association and the National Institute of Health, as well as private sector companies (Monsanto, Procter and Gamble, Bayer, Pfizer, Dow Chemical) are not doing anything to stop the insanity. Bottom line: profits trump health in this country. Pharmaceutical medications and vaccinations are the main way many doctors tackle health conditions. However, both can be toxic and are often not needed if you educate yourself; and take preventative measures of keeping up a healthy diet by exercising, getting quality sleep, taking basic supplementation and managing stress.

Our bodies have an inherent detoxification system, but the rate and volume of what we are being exposed to is breaking down our immune tolerance. Each person's body is different; some of us can handle more heavy metal exposure, some more food additives, but in the end the cumulative effect is a weakened immune system leading to poor health. Thyroid imbalances such as hypothyroidism, nodules, and autoimmune Hashimoto's disease are skyrocketing because of higher levels of radiation, heavy metals, pesticides and xenoestrogens. The United States is one of the sickest nations. Who's going to rescue us? Don't wait for your government or doctor to educate you. Until the existing paradigm collapses and greed is no longer the primary motivation, not much will change in our healthcare system.

Conditions Directly or Indirectly Caused by
Candida/Fungal Overgrowth
(FIGURE 1)

Autoimmune Diseases
Chronic Fatigue Syndrome
Fibromyalgia
HIV/AIDS
Hodgkin's Disease
Leukemia
Multiple Sclerosis
Muscular Dystrophy
Myasthenia Gravis
Rheumatoid Arthritis
Sarcoidosis
Scleroderma
Systemic Lupus Erythematous
Blood System
Chronic Infections
Iron Deficiency
Thrombocytopenic Purpura
Cancer
Cardiovascular
Endocarditis
Mitral Valve Prolapse
Valve Problems
Digestive System
Anorexia Nervosa
Bloating
Carbohydrate/Sugar Cravings
Colitis
Constipation
Crohn's Disease
Diarrhea
Dysbiosis
Food Allergies
Gastritis
Heartburn
Intestinal Pain
Malabsorption
Maldigestion
Endocrine System
Adrenal/Thyroid failure
Diabetes
Hormonal Imbalances
Hypoglycemia
Insomnia
Over/Under Weight
Nervous System
Alcoholism
Anxiety

Attention Deficit Disorder
Autism
Brain Fog
Depression
Headaches
Hyperirritability
Hyperactivity
Learning Difficulties
Manic-Depressive Disorder
Memory Loss
Migraines
Schizophrenia
Suicidal
Respiratory System/
Ears/Eyes/Mouth
Asthma
Bronchitis
Dizziness
Earaches
Env. Allergies/
Chemical Sensitivities
Hay Fever
Oral Thrush
Sinusitis
Skin
Acne
Diaper Rash
Dry Skin and Itching
Eczema
Hives
Hair loss
Leprosy
Liver spots
Psoriasis
Urinary/Reproductive (Female/Male)
Cystitis
Endometriosis
Fibroids
Impotence
Loss of Libido
Menstrual Irregularities
PMS
Prostitis
Sexually Transmitted
Urethritis
Yeast Vaginal Infections
Virus
Epstein Barr Virus

Nutritional Deficiency and Toxicity in the Body

The third major disruptor to the body is food. In the United States, the FDA allows 3,000 food additives and chemicals to infuse our food supply. Our soils are full of pesticides, herbicides and fungicides, and are planted with genetically modified seeds. Even when eating healthy food, you need to eat 5 to 10 times what your grandparents ate to attain the same nutritional value as they were getting. Foods are processed and can contain high fructose corn syrup, trans-fats and preservatives. Fast food chains make it easy, convenient and affordable to feed your family, but you are getting nothing but empty calories and taking the fast track toward inflammation in the body.

And why are we overeating? One reason is the portions we are served in restaurants are often big enough for two or three meals. We don't need quantity; we need quality. Another reason is that too often we use food as an emotional pacifier to deal with fear-based emotions. Lastly, people tend to overeat because they are malnourished. People who eat poorly eat more because their body is literally not getting enough nutrients from junk food, and thus crave more food to function properly. How can a body thrive when you are putting trash into it? It cannot!

Stress — The Number One Body Breaker

Unmanaged stress is the fourth cause of inflammation. We all have some level of stress but how well do we manage it? Do you get seven to eight hours of quality sleep? Do you engage in weekly exercise? Do you meditate regularly? Do you make time for your favorite hobby or spend time in nature? Or do you find your mind is racing with worries, what ifs, shoulds and coulds? Are you waking up depressed and anxious, feeling that your life is overwhelming and devoid of passion and purpose?

Most of us do not live in the present moment. This creates tremendous stress. We are living in the past carrying negative emotions, or living in the future filled with fear-based thoughts and pressured with many unfinished projects. We are pushing to make ends meet and exhausted most of the time. Unmanaged stress will break a body down *even if* you are eating right and exercising.

What Is Creating Inflammation?	
Infections Candida, Fungus, Viruses, Parasites, Bacteria	**Poor Diet/Nutritional Deficiencies** Refined sugars, Alcohol, Dairy, Caffeine, Gluten and Refined flours, Corn, Soy, Trans fats, Preservatives, Lack of water
Gastrointestinal Imbalances Maldigestion, Malabsorption, Elimination problems, Intestinal dysbiosis, Compromised liver function, Leaky gut	**Environmental Toxicity** Pesticides, Herbicides, Fungicides, Plastics, Amalgam fillings, Heavy metals, Mold, Petroleum particulates, Noise pollution, Electromagnetic fields
Mental/Emotional Stress Negative/fearful thoughts & emotions, Addictions	**Spiritual Disconnection** Outdated beliefs, No hope, Isolation, Lack of love
Pharmaceutical medications Overuse of Antibiotics, Steroids, NSAID's, Vaccinations	**Physical stress** Trauma, Lack of exercise, Lack of sleep
Genes Phenotype	

WHAT CAN I DO TO TAKE CONTROL OF MY HEALTH?

You might say "I'm throwing in the towel—all of this information is overwhelming." The key is to do what is in your control. Start with baby steps and slowly build into creating a healthy lifestyle for you and your family, consisting of eating healthy, exercising, detoxifying the body, taking supplements and managing stress.

Healthy Diet

Food is designed to give you optimal energy. To achieve that goal your diet ideally needs to be 60% vegetables, 20% protein, 15% gluten-free whole grains, beans, and legumes, and 5% good fats and fruits. Start eliminating or reducing your alcohol, sugar, gluten, corn, soy and dairy consumption, which are the biggest culprits in making you symptomatic. Shop at your local farmer's markets, health food stores, and online sites that sell healthier foods and snacks. Learn to cook and eat more meals at home. Read ingredients on everything—you will be amazed at the amount of sugars, salt, and preservatives that are in your packaged food.

Eat a rainbow of vegetables and make dark, leafy greens a part of your daily diet to take in their many beneficial phytochemicals. Some of your vegetable consumption can be juiced or put into a Vitamix or NutriBullet to make smoothies. When juicing, use organic vegetables when possible and make sure the bulk of your juice is celery, cucumber, and dark leafy greens (e.g., spinach, watercress, parsley, cilantro, green lettuces, and kale). Avoid using large quantities of sweet vegetables such as carrots and beets or too much fruit, which will feed candida and disrupt blood sugar levels in the body. Incorporate fresh herbs, spices, and sea vegetables, such as rosemary, parsley, thyme, turmeric, ginger, and various seaweeds on a daily basis to offset inflammation and infection, move out heavy metals, and replenish minerals in the body.

Buy organic, grass-fed, antibiotic- and hormone-free animal protein. Eat only 2 to 4 ounces at a time. Eggs are best poached, sunny side up or soft-boiled. Stick with wild fish, not farmed. Wild salmon, trout, cod, sole and other white fishes are a good choice. Do not eat tuna of any kind because of high mercury levels.

Gluten-free grains are a better choice for everyone versus those with gluten. In the United States, 90% of corn is genetically modified and wheat has been hybridized. The wheat seed is not the same as it was fifty years ago and is wreaking havoc in everyone's body to some degree. I encourage switching to amaranth, brown rice, buckwheat, kaniwa, millet, gluten-free oats, quinoa, teff and wild rice.

Beans and legumes are best when organic and soaked in water overnight. Limit them to small portions once or twice a week. They do have protein and fiber but are also high in starch, which turns into sugar rapidly and feeds candida. This can be more inflammatory to people who suffer from pain or autoimmune conditions.

Good fats consisting of raw seeds, nuts, nut butters, coconut and olive oils, avocados, and organic, unsalted grass-fed butter in small amounts are essential for a healthy brain, heart, skin and endocrine system. Avoid peanuts and peanut butter as they contain aflatoxins (mold toxins), which are highly carcinogenic.

Most people find that dairy products cause chronic gastrointestinal distress, sinusitis, and ear and respiratory congestion. Dairy substitutes such as unsweetened almond, coconut, or hemp milk are good replacements for cow's milk. Some people can tolerate small amounts of raw (i.e., not pasteurized) goat or sheep cheese.

I recommend limiting fruits to one or two per day and they should be organic when possible. Even though fruit has natural sugar, too much will elevate blood sugar and contribute to hypoglycemia (low blood sugar) or hyperglycemia (diabetes). I prefer fruits with a low glycemic index, such as berries, green apples, grapefruit, coconut flesh, lemon/limes, and avocados. Avoid dried fruits and fruit juices because they are higher in sugar.

Drink purified water and herbal and green tea instead of coffee, soda, fruit juice or lattes. Put fresh lemon or lime into your water to help alkalize your body. After changing your nutrition you may very well find that you can reduce the amount of medications you might be taking or you may no longer need medication at all (make sure you check with your physician first). You will also find that ailments, aches, rashes and inflammation you once had are now gone.

Detox Your Body

Your gastrointestinal tract has 100 trillion cells, about ten times more cells than make up the rest of the body. It is also where 75% of your immune system resides. As explained above, most disease starts from microbial overgrowth and/or absence of good bacteria, called dysbiosis. If you want to take your health to the next level, read my book *The Candida Cure*, which sets forth a 90-day program to detoxify your body from years of poor lifestyle habits and restore your health. My program will remove infections such as candida, bacteria, and parasites; balance blood sugar levels and adrenal function; cleanse your blood, liver, kidneys and lymphatic system; and help restore vitality to your organs. Everyone today needs to clean the slate from years of stored toxins. My program is an easy way to do that and will help you age with quality.

Ionic Footbaths and Saunas

To stay healthy, we need to move toxins out of the body as fast as they accumulate. Ionic footbaths work with negative and positive ions, and help remove heavy metals and other inflammatory agents from the body. They kill bacteria and fungus on contact, increase oxygen in the body, increase blood circulation, promote restful sleep, and relieve pain. Doing a footbath once a week can help neutralize the assault on our bodies from environmental toxins and poor diet. Dry, steam, and infrared saunas are another great way to detoxify the body.

Exercise

Your bloodstream and lymphatic system are the rivers that keep toxins moving out the body and assist getting nutrients in. Lack of movement and lazy breathing lead to poor circulation and lymphatic congestion. We are all at different stages of our lives and different exercise appeals to each of us - tune into what would feel best for your body right now. For some it will be going to the gym or playing a favorite sport. Others might find yoga, walking, swimming, or tai chi more engaging. If you are not ambulatory, do isometric and breathing exercises. Exercising three to five times a week will increase endorphins and move waste out of the body.

Breathing

Daily deep breathing exercises are extremely beneficial. Many people are shallow breathers and even hold their breath for periods of time throughout the day. Proper exhalation accounts for 75% of how we move waste out of the body. Breathing cleanses you, centers you, and keeps you in the "now" moment, which is your place of power. Investigate Pranayama breathing techniques—practicing these will teach you how to breathe properly. Do not discount proper breathing. It is a powerful tool that increases oxygen in the body, and balances both the body and mind.

Quality Sleep

Everyone is talking about anti-aging. The first and foremost way to age with quality is to get seven to nine hours of uninterrupted sleep. Make sure to power off all electronics and make your bedroom as dark as possible to assist your pineal gland in secreting an optimal amount of melatonin. If you have difficulty falling asleep, steep organic chamomile tea in water for 20 minutes and drink it one hour before going to bed. If possible, sleep with your head facing magnetic north to offset inflammation from electromagnetic frequencies.

Supplementation

Since we are living in a time when we can't obtain all our nutrients from our diet, I suggest some basic supplementation. Buy quality supplements, organic foods, organic body care products and green house care products, which are available at discount prices on websites such as vitacost.com, iherb.com, and amazon.com. I recommend a good quality multivitamin/multimineral without iron and chelated minerals, extra vitamin C (one with minerals and/or bioflavonoids), extra vitamin E with mixed tocopherols and tocotrienols, a free-form amino acid blend, omega 3 fish oil, evening primrose oil for women, an antioxidant formula (such as Antioxidant Extreme by HealthForce Nutritionals), and a superfood powder (such as Nanogreens or Macrogreens).

Chemical Round Up

Get rid of the toxic body care products, cleaning supplies, laundry detergents, fabric softeners, air fresheners, fertilizers and insecticides. The more chemicals you take in, the more toxic you are. Look through your body care items (shampoos, conditioners, body wash, perfumes, deodorants, toothpastes and body lotions) and replace any that have parabens, sodium laureth sulfate, phthalates and artificial fragrances. You can find healthier, non-toxic products at your local health market or online at amazon.com and vitacost.com. Replace nonstick cookware with stainless steel or enameled, cast iron cookware. Clean out the garage and get rid of pesticides, herbicides (Round Up), varnishes, lead paint and other toxic chemicals. Replace them with organic fertilizers and investigate natural pest control methods on the Internet. Buy a water and air purification system for your house. Put plants in your house and bedroom to oxygenate your home.

PSYCHOLOGICAL SELF & MANAGING STRESS

Health is not just about eating healthy and taking vitamins. It is critical to nurture the emotional, mental and spiritual parts of you. Neutralizing negative and worrisome thoughts and releasing fear-based emotions such as anger, sadness, and guilt as well as connecting spiritually to what you believe in will create the whole picture of balance in your life. In other words, put yourself first on the list. Take 5 to 20 extra minutes each day and do some of the suggestions below to set the tone for your day; and bring about more joy and health.

Meditation

Meditation is a practice that I feel is not just a suggestion but also a necessity to neutralize today's stressors. Meditation does not conflict with religious beliefs and can become a daily, nurturing part of your routine. Meditation is so powerful because it balances all parts of us: physically, emotionally, mentally, and spiritually. Whether you sit for 5 or 20 minutes a day, it will not take long for you to feel the positive difference it is making in your life.

Challenge Outdated Belief Systems

How many of us stop to challenge our belief systems about health, work, money, and our relationships with self and others? Beliefs are the foundation of how your life will turn out, but they are not laws written in stone. Most beliefs are worn out hand-me-downs from our parents or society that we just accepted. Begin to investigate and challenge those areas that are not working for you. Here are some questions to help you examine a belief system that you feel might be holding you back. Pick a specific topic and ask: Does my present belief system make me happy? Do these beliefs ring true for me at this time? Does this belief keep me inflexible? Is this belief a hand-me-down from parents or society that I took in as a child? Does this belief augment my life and serve others?

You will quickly discover what you feel and can then decide whether to hold onto that belief or change it. To change it, make a conscious choice to do so. Then affirm it mentally and emotionally each day until it becomes yours. Accepting a new belief is just like adopting a new diet. It takes time to see the changes manifest.

When I was diagnosed with multiple sclerosis at the age of 24, the doctor said to me, "The good news is you don't have cancer; the bad news is that you have multiple sclerosis. We have chemotherapy and you can expect to be in a wheelchair." Had I held onto that belief, I would not have survived.

Honor Yourself

Bring more joy and laughter into your life. Move out of being a perfectionist and picking yourself apart. Accept what is and know there is room for growth. Pat yourself on the back regularly for giving it your best. Laugh at yourself and life. Let go more often, forgive daily, and play like the child you once were. Be grateful and focus on what you do have, not what you don't have. Living in gratitude means a life with more ease and grace.

CONCLUSION

The world, our healthcare systems, and our financial structures look bleak right now, but as each one of us wakes up and takes responsibility for our own lives and helps educate others, we will create a brighter future. Continue to connect with one another. Social networking (Facebook, Twitter, the Internet) is one great way we can educate each other and collectively demand better agricultural practices; support the integration of alternative and Western medicine; and encourage more evolved educational systems that also focus on health, nutrition, and psychological well-being.

Never give up hope. Trust and believe that your life, your body, and this world can be better. Visualize and send healing energy to yourself, those you care about, the planet, and the people of the world. We are all on this ride together. It is only through acceptance, forgiveness, compassion, collaboration, tenacity and creativity that we can have healthier and happier lives. Know that you make a difference in the world. You are in the driver's seat and you deserve the best ride possible.

CHAPTER 3

Dr. Bradley Nelson

Time Heals All Wounds? Perhaps Not...

You've probably heard it said that time heals all wounds, but this is not necessarily true. You may think you have let go of all your emotional pain from prior relationships, and maybe you've had therapy to deal with it. It may seem like it's all behind you now, but your body can literally be inhabited by the invisible energies of old emotions. These are wounds that time alone cannot and will not heal. They can cause you to act and feel differently in your current relationships and may even cause you to sabotage them.

When a trapped emotion is released, a burden is literally lifted. In fact, people often experience a feeling of lightness upon the release of a trapped emotion. Finding and releasing those trapped negative energies can literally make changes in how you feel and behave, in the choices that you make, and in the results that you get.

Over the course of my years as a chiropractor, specializing in energy healing, I developed a method for helping my patients locate, identify, and release negative energies that had become lodged in various parts of their bodies, resulting in pain and disease.

This method, called "The Emotion Code, is about clearing away this past baggage, so that you can be who you really are inside. You are not your emotional baggage, but sometimes your trapped emotions can derail you, or cause you to travel on paths you'd rather not take. Trapped emotions can keep you from living the vibrant, healthy life you are meant to live.

Trapped Emotions and Physical Pain

In addition to obvious emotional pain, millions of people are suffering from physical aches and pains. Many times there are unseen trapped emotional energies that contribute to or create physical pain.

The next example illustrates how trapped emotions can exert an astonishingly powerful influence over the physical body.

Debbie's Broken Heart

Debbie had been a patient of mine for a year or so, when one day she came into my office complaining of what she thought might be a heart attack. She had chest pain and difficulty breathing; her left arm was completely numb, as was the left side of her face. She said it had been gradually getting worse for about 24 hours. I immediately had her lie down and put my staff on alert that we may need medical assistance. After checking her vital signs and finding them to be normal, I tested her body to see if these symptoms were being caused by a trapped emotion. The answer her body gave was "Yes."

I continued to test Debbie, and quickly determined that the trapped emotion was heartache. A little more testing revealed that this emotion had become trapped in her body three years earlier. At this point she burst into tears and exclaimed, "I thought I'd dealt with all that in therapy! I can't believe that is showing up now!" I asked, "Can you share what happened?"

She replied that three years before, her husband had an affair. The news was devastating to her. It destroyed her marriage and wrecked her life for a while, but she gradually came to terms with it. She cried a lot of tears, spent a year in therapy, got remarried, and moved on - or so she thought.

Debbie expressed surprise that her past heartache was still affecting her, and in such a dramatic way. How could this event be the source of her physical pain when she'd gone to such lengths to deal with it already? She had done all the things we're told to do. She'd cried and expressed her feelings, sought the comfort of friends and the advice of therapists, opened up a dialogue with her husband and reconciled with her divorce. It had not been easy and she'd made a lot of important progress. In her mind she'd dealt with it and put it behind her.

What she didn't see is what none of us can see. There was a physical effect from her experience that was silent and invisible until she began to manifest symptoms from it. She had dealt with her troubles in every way but this. She was suffering from a trapped emotion.

I released the trapped heartache from her body, and within seconds the feeling came back into her arm and into her face. Suddenly she could breathe freely and the chest pain and heaviness were gone. She left the office shortly after, feeling completely fine.

The overwhelming heartache that she had felt during those early days of her breakup had literally become trapped in her physical body. The instantaneous relief of her physical symptoms was astounding to me. I was left to ponder on the mechanism that was at work here. How could a single trapped emotion cause such extreme physical symptoms?

Debbie's experience is a dramatic example of how trapped emotions can affect us physically, and how traditional therapy cannot and does not attempt to remove them, although traditional therapy certainly has its place. Typically, trapped emotions will not cause symptoms as intense as the ones that Debbie experienced. Most are more subtle, yet exert an imbalancing influence on both mind and body.

Sharon's Mother was a Pain

A patient named Sharon came to my office one day complaining of pain in her abdomen. She told me that the pain felt like it was coming from her right ovary. I tested her to see if the cause of her pain was due to a trapped emotion, and found that it was.

Further testing revealed that the exact emotion was frustration, that it had to do with her mother, and that it had become trapped in her body three days earlier. The moment I arrived at this determination, she became quite upset and angrily hissed, "Oh, my mother! She called me three days ago, and dumped all of this stuff on me! I wish she would just get out of my life, and leave me alone!"

I released the trapped frustration from her body and the pain instantly vanished. Sharon was amazed, and could hardly believe that the pain was entirely and suddenly gone. Even more amazing to Sharon was the fact that her intense frustration with her mother was the apparent cause of the physical pain she had been suffering from for the last three days.

Trapped emotions can even create muscular imbalances that lead to joint malfunction and eventual joint degeneration and arthritis. I have seen hundreds of cases where acute physical pain instantly left the body upon the release of a trapped emotion.

Jim's Bad Knees

Removing trapped emotions can often relieve pain and suffering, even in cases that would be considered hopeless by conventional medicine. This is a letter I received from a former patient whose case certainly fits this description.

I was your patient for a few years and know that I had many physical problems with my legs, knees and back when I came to you. I was able to withstand the side effects of the various supplements you prescribed to cleanse my system and then through your abilities to release the resentments, anger and fear that I was hanging on to, we were able to achieve a physical position where my knees stopped hurting (I had been told by my doctor that replaced my hips that my knees needed replacing because they were worn out also) and I was able to walk, climb stairs, etc. pain-free for the first time in years. To this day I am basically active and pain-free. This is not to say that arthritis doesn't come into play as I continue to grow older, but the worn-out knees are still working fine and for that I am grateful. I wish you the best with your book and pray that it can open the door for others to a healthy life.

Keep the faith, Jim H.

People often put up with their pain, and end up simply "living with it", especially when they cannot find a solution or a reason for it. Pain is the body's way of telling you there is a problem; it's a warning sign.

In my experience of working with people in pain, I've observed that trapped emotions are actually creating the pain at least 50% of the time.

Pinned to the Past

I was teaching a workshop once in Las Vegas when I had an interesting experience. I asked for a volunteer, and a young woman in her early twenties came up out of the audience. I asked her if she had any particular physical complaints, and she said no, that she was healthy, and had no problems. I muscle tested her to see if she had a trapped emotion, and she did. The emotion was unsupported, which is a feeling similar to being all alone, and without help when you really need it.

Through muscle testing I asked her body when this emotion had become trapped. I asked, "Did this emotion become trapped within the last five years?" "No." "Did this emotion become trapped between ages ten and twenty?" "No." "Did this emotion become trapped between ages birth to ten?" "Yes." "Did this emotion become trapped in the first five years of your life?" "Yes." "Did this emotion become trapped in the first year of your life?" "Yes." "Did this emotion occur after one year of age?" "No." I asked her if she had any idea what this might be about, and she shook her head no.

It just so happened that this young woman had arrived at the workshop with her mother, and they had been sitting together in the audience. At this point, I looked out at the audience and noticed that her mother looked very uncomfortable. Her hand was covering her mouth and she looked either frightened or very embarrassed, I couldn't tell which. I asked her if she knew what might have happened, since her daughter was too young to remember.

In a very pained and embarrassed voice she explained, "Well, when Jessica was a baby I used cloth diapers, which I would close with safety pins. There was one particular occasion where, I'm ashamed to say, that I accidently pinned her to her diaper. She cried and cried, but I didn't realize that she was pinned to her diaper until I changed her again. I can't believe this is showing up now, and I felt so horrible about this and I still do."

I turned to Jessica and asked, "Is that what this trapped emotion is about?" I pressed down on her arm and it was very strong, indicating that this was indeed the case. I released the trapped emotional energy by rolling three times down her back with a magnet, and she sat down again. About two weeks later I received the following e-mail:

Hi Dr. Brad,
When you were in Las Vegas, you cleared a trapped emotion for my daughter, Jessica, stemming from infancy. Jessica has suffered from hip and knee pain since about the age of 12 years...it has gotten worse as she got older. Since you worked on clearing her trapped emotion of feeling unsupported (about 1 1/2 weeks ago), she has had no pain or

constriction in her hips and knees. She has never gone more than a day or two without pain, and because it was worsening, it was beginning to affect her gait. She is ecstatic, and now is experiencing a "new" sense of inner joy. She sends her heartfelt thanks.
Jessica said feel free to share her story....she is certainly telling everyone in Las Vegas about it!
Thank you! - Maureen C.

Here is another example of a trapped emotion creating physical pain. The event that caused the trapped emotion happened when Jessica was a baby, and she had no conscious memory of it. Had we not released it, I believe that Jessica may have eventually become disabled, and the true cause of her disability – her trapped emotion – would have remained undiscovered. Of course, not all physical pain is caused by trapped emotions. But isn't it interesting to contemplate that they can cause or contribute to physical pain? I have come to understand that trapped emotions seem to be involved, to one degree or another, in nearly every illness I have encountered. How is this possible?

Trapped Emotions and Disease

The most ancient idea in the art of healing is that disease is caused by imbalance in the body. Trapped emotions are perhaps the most common type of imbalance that human beings suffer from. I believe that trapped emotions can be implicated in nearly all diseases, either directly or indirectly. Because trapped emotions are nearly universal, and because they always create distortion in the energy field of the body, and because they are completely invisible, they can cause an incredibly wide variety of physical problems without being unmasked.

Acid Reflux	Diabetes	Learning Disabilities
ADD/ADHD	Dyslexia	Low Back Pain
Allergies	Eye Pain	Hypothyroidism
Abdominal Pain	Fibromyalgia	Lupus
Asthma	Frigidity	Migraines
Back Pain	Headaches	Multiple Sclerosis
Bell's Palsy	Heartburn (GERD)	Neck pain
Cancer	Hip Pain	Night Terrors
Carpal Tunnel	Hypoglycemia	Panic Attacks
Chest Pain	Impotency	Parkinson's disease
Chronic Fatigue	Infertility	Phobias
Chron's Disease	Insomnia	Shoulder pain
Colitis	Irritable Bowel (IBS)	Sinus problems
Constipation	Joint Pain	Tennis Elbow
Depression	Knee Pain	Vertigo

Trapped emotions are truly epidemic, and are the insidious, invisible cause of much suffering and illness, both physical and emotional in nature.

Trapped emotions lower immune function and make the body more vulnerable to disease. They can distort body tissues, block the flow of energy, and prevent normal function of organs and glands. On the following page is a list of conditions and diseases that my patients came to me with, where trapped emotions appeared as a contributing factor and, many times, as the entire cause of the condition.

I am not saying that releasing trapped emotions is a cure-all. "The Emotion Code" should not be used by itself in attempting to address any major disease or medical condition; but it should be looked upon as an adjunctive therapy. When trapped emotions are contributing to physical illness, removing them can only help.

"The Emotion Code" is easy to use and precise. Sometimes the release of a trapped emotion will bring about an instantaneous and dramatic effect, but most of the time the effects are more subtle; yet they always seem to bring a greater sense of contentment and peace, whether they are immediate or gradual.

If you are like many of the people who have come to my seminars over the years, using "The Emotion Code" will bring a new joy and freedom to your life.

It will give you a greater feeling of serenity because you will be freeing yourself from your old emotional baggage. The results can bring balance, a new inner calm and profound healing where nothing else has helped before.

CHAPTER 4

Dorothy M. Neddermeyer, PhD

Breast Health – Prevention: The Answer To Cancer

The truth is in spite of sixty-plus years of research, chemotherapy, radiation, breasts removed, walking for breast cancer, pink ribbons and parties for breast cancer, cancer is on the rise. The biggest medical myth is that mammograms prevent cancer by early detection. How can a mammogram prevent cancer when a mammogram is used to detect cancer?

To prevent anything, one needs to understand how it is created. We live in a three-dimensional world made up of Universal Laws. Universal Laws are founded on the understanding that everything in the universe is energy, including humans, and that energy moves in a circular fashion. At the microscopic level, every living thing is a whirling mass of electrons and energy atoms spinning rapidly. Humans are intimately connected with this sea of whirling electrons.

Our beliefs, thoughts, feelings, words and actions are forms of energy. What we believe, think, feel, say and do in each moment comes back to us to create our realities. Energy moves in a circle, so what goes around comes around. The combined beliefs, thoughts, feelings, words and actions of everyone on the planet creates our collective consciousness; it creates the world we see. Mind, Body, Spirit, health is your birth right. It is you responsibility to yourself to maintain what is rightfully yours.

Health is our natural state of being. Disease is abnormal and can't exist in a healthy body. Remove the thoughts of victim, fear, worry, war, disease, etc., and the thoughts are deleted from the collective thought cesspool. Your "search engine" will come up with nothing. Spell check makes sure words are spelled right. Empower yourself by using a "thought check" system for the next 30 days and see how your life changes. Allow only thoughts of health, joy, peace, integrity and harmony. Watch how everything changes. Avoid allowing the pharmaceutical and medical professions to scare you into believing you will get a disease because you are a certain age, or you are 'genetically' predisposed to have a particular disease.

You have greater control of your health than you know. I know first-hand and from the experience of my clients, whom I assist in transforming dire dis-eases – Cancer, Diabetes, Lupus, Hepatitis C, Fibromyalgia, MS, High Blood Pressure, Mitral Valve Prolapse, Bipolar, Anxiety, Panic, PTSD, and the list goes on.

Nothing can be transformed [healed] through a process of 'fighting against it.' First we need to look at how the existence of disease – and in fact, reality in general - are created.

Thoughts are created from our indoctrination and conditioning whereby feelings and actions follow. Thoughts and feelings are impulses of energy. The human body is made up of trillions of cells receiving these impulses. Cells of the nervous system, called nerve cells or neurons, are specialized to carry "messages" from these impulses through an electrochemical process. The human brain has approximately 100 billion of these neurons.

Neurons have specialized projections called dendrites and axons. Dendrites bring information to the cell body and axons take information away from the cell body. Information from one neuron flows to another neuron across a synapse. The synapse is a small gap separating neurons. The synapse consists of:

1. A pre-synaptic ending that contains neurotransmitters, mitochondria and other cell organelles,
2. A post-synaptic ending that contains receptor sites for neurotransmitters and,
3. A synaptic cleft or space between the pre-synaptic and post-synaptic endings.

Thoughts and feelings are impulses of energy and information. They send out vibrational pictures, patterns, and colors (not words or language). This energy affects the atmosphere (energy field) around the person thinking the thought or feeling the feeling. Once these impulses go out they can never be retracted. What we see in the outer world is a reflection of collective humanity's thoughts and feelings.

Radio, TV programming and popular publications create your future. It's simple to understand how reality is created when you understand the Science of Consciousness. But what is consciousness and how can you influence it? Collective consciousness is the sum total of humanity's beliefs, thoughts, feelings and actions. Media, public relations firms, and advertising constantly send out thought-forms that program us for sickness, drugs, violence, fear, and materiality. These thoughts go into collective consciousness and create a huge cesspool of dysfunctional beliefs from which we draw our personal thoughts. And, in regard to pharmaceutical and medical practices, perception is carefully and precisely regulated.

Most conventional wisdom is implanted into the public consciousness by a thousand contrived media clips per day. Whose Thoughts Are You Thinking? Where your attention goes, your reality is created. Have you wondered why most people in any society generally think the same thing about most issues? Have you wondered why an entire community has a high incidence of a particular disease? These perceptions are perpetrated and continuously reinforced by spin doctors. The thought is created first, then it manifests in everyday life. For example, constant awareness to medical problems creates more drug customers – thus it is good business to promote a "disease de jour".

Cancer was rare until fear thoughts were programmed into consciousness. People did not think about flu shots until the media promoted them. Have you ever wondered about the ethics of TV Allergy Reports being sponsored by a drug company? Do you believe allergy medicine will cure allergies or are pharmaceuticals a profit- making industry? What's true is that awareness to allergies promotes allergies. Remove those thoughts from your energy field and your allergies will be gone.

Let's explore conventional thought streams highly promoted, which create public consciousness:

1. An education guarantees financial success
2. War will create peace
3. Fluoride protects your teeth
4. Be afraid of sun causing cancer
5. Awareness of a disease prevents the disease
6. Mammograms prevent breast cancer
7. The economy is bad – doom is near
8. The economy is good – time to spend freely

Do yourself a favor, 'Dare To Think For Your Self' even though you might be considered wacky, a Pollyanna or worse, out of touch with reality. Thinking for yourself is healthier than allowing yourself to be programmed to have all the diseases the pharmaceutical companies want you to have so they can sell drugs.

"We cannot create solutions to problems with the same consciousness that created them."–Einstein.

"Doing the same thing over and over and expecting different results is the definition of insanity."–Einstein.

The American Cancer Society estimates breast cancer in men in the United States for 2012:

- Approximately 2,190 new cases of invasive breast cancer will be diagnosed among men
- Approximately 410 men will die from breast cancer
- The lifetime risk of breast cancer is about 1 in 1,000 for men. The number of breast cancer cases in men relative to the population has been fairly stable for the last 30 years.

Men are being programmed to have breast cancer. Check breast cancer statistics in men in 2017.

The American Cancer Society estimates breast cancer in the United States in 2012 will be approximately:

- 226,870 cases of invasive breast cancer in women
- 63,000 cases of carcinoma in situ (CIS – non-invasive and is the earliest form of breast cancer) will be found

- 39,510 deaths from breast cancer (women)

Breast cancer is the second leading cause of cancer death in women, after lung cancer. The chance of women dying from breast cancer is approximately 1 in 36. There are more than 2.5 million breast cancer survivors in the U.S. The American Cancer Society's prediction of breast cancer cases for 2012 is fueling the belief of millions of women. These statistics are good marketing tools for pharmaceutical companies, doctors, hospitals and hospices.

When you understand the truth about how reality is created, you will think beyond living in only a "physical world", and think in terms of an "energy world." To break free of collective programming, you will need to shift your thought programming, and then vigilantly select each thought and feeling. Shifting your thought programming is much like installing an upgraded program onto your computer. "Fighting Against" Energy Creates More Of What You Don't Want and Collapses Your Energy Field.

The Internet has connected the world. You send e-mail via the Internet. Likewise, you are constantly sending people "energy mail" messages. It does not matter whether the person is in the same room or across the globe. They instantly, consciously or unconsciously, get your "energy mail." To create the reality you prefer, you need to be very selective with each thought you allow to enter your mind, and carefully monitor the thoughts and feelings you send to others. "Hedging Against" and "Ruminating." To Protect Yourself from something is creating what you DO NOT desire. Most people have been programmed to hedge against inflation, to purchase insurance to protect against disability, fire, death, illness, etc. The "save for a rainy day" mindset is also "hedging against." This attracts to you what you don't want in your life. The hidden motivation to save for retirement is usually driven by a desire to protect against old age.

The mind set of "AGAINST vs. FOR" profits huge industries. People buy products and get medical tests and check-ups for the negative reasons of protecting themselves. All of the above scenarios are fear-based motivations that disempower you, collapse your energy field and create the opposite of your intentions.

Well-intended participants are running or walking, etc, with the intent to 'find a cancer cure' or honor someone they know/knew, who experienced cancer. What they have not understood is that by putting these thoughts into their minds, the disease gets created. What if people knew they get what they are thinking and feeling, not what they think they are thinking and feeling … AND that whatever they give attention to will expand. Would they still participate? Words and feelings are powerful creators of reality. Avoid putting cancer thoughts in your consciousness (consciously or unconsciously)–you won't create cancer in your life. A magnet does not stick to wood–only to metal. Remove the thoughts from millions of people's consciousness (and even from your family genetic consciousness)- and the disease seldom manifests or conditions disappear.

Your brain can't hold two thoughts simultaneously. You can't simultaneously hold a happy and sad thought, or healthy and sick thought. It's impossible to think about "Fighting Breast Cancer" and simultaneously hold the thought of total health and vibrant aliveness. So what are you doing when you are fighting against something? The answer is, the more attention you put on the disease, the more people experience it.

Think about this, nearly every grocery store has a pharmacy. The conscious message is food and pharmaceuticals go hand-in-hand to keep the body well. Is there any question why hospitals, doctors and pharmaceutical companies continue to bombard consciousness with what they want to create – more patients?

Consider instead: A Walk For Peace in Celebration of the United Nations; Walking the Camino for the purpose of a spiritual and physical challenge, and with the intention to find one's deepest "spiritual meaning"; then write a book about it, as Shirley McClaine did. Can you hear the difference in the motivations and energetic vibration?

These examples FOR health and FOR positive intention are very different motivations than fear, doom and sickness-laden messages. Polarized Thinking Presenting information with polarized viewpoints is another way to increase negative results through creating apathy. The back and forth bantering does the same thing to your psyche as a cat that bats a mouse back and forth until it's lethargic. Many people today are confused and don't know who to believe or what to trust. This is the result of strategic spin doctors who practice the science of creating controversial public opinion. They can put a particular product or concept in a desirable light. They know the best public relations takes place when people are unaware that they are being manipulated. To create public opinion PR firms select specific radio, TV, magazines and newspapers and use attack strategies and third party endorsements by institutes, foundations, celebrities, scientists for hire, etc. The media also uses press releases from pharmaceutical companies, ostensibly as investigative news. The sole purpose of press releases as news is to keep you in fear and uncertainty so you will watch again, and be subjected to more advertising and more fear. Polarized talk show participants keep consciousness stuck in no-win thought patterns.

There is a disease of the month celebrated every month. What are we creating when we celebrate a disease? What do you think Breast Cancer Awareness month will create - more health or disease? Do you want to be part of the problem, or part of the solution? Think about this and then determine what you will do.

Who You Are and What You Do Makes A Difference. "We are not only responsible for what we do, but also, for that what we don't do."–Voltaire

One of the greatest gifts you can give yourself is to monitor everything we think and feel. Stop reading popular magazines and newspapers…stop watching TV and listening to radio cancer commercials…and you will be amazed at how different you think and feel.

There are eight strategies to create health:

1. Think for yourself. Take care of yourself first. The airline flight attendants instruct adults to put on their oxygen masks first before helping children and others. There is a practical reason for that: an oxygen-deprived brain does not function clearly. Therefore, the adults must be properly oxygenated to provide assistance. Similarly, if your health and wellbeing are compromised, you are unable to be of full benefit to those who count on your care.

2. Shift your consciousness to create Health instead of fighting/guarding against a disease.
3. Focus on positive thoughts.
4. Expand and maintain Spiritual Enlightenment – Meditate, Ti Chi, Yoga
5. Consistently create peace of mind and joy.
6. Maintain a healthy food plan for your blood type; plus vitamins and supplements.
    a. Maintain an alkaline system. Cancer is unable to exist in an alkaline environment.
    b. Eliminate WHEAT
    c. Consume 4 to 5 servings of raw vegetables per day
    d. Consume 2 to 3 servings of Monounsaturated Fatty Acids per day.
    e. Consume 8 to 10 8-oz. glasses of water per day.
7. Exercise 2 to 3 times per week
8. Engage in leisure pursuits – hobbies, sports, etc.

It takes great courage to pull out of the cesspool of dysfunctional thinking and processed or fast food mania, and live the Universal Laws of truth. It's time to wake up and take responsibility for your health, wellness and happiness.

What we envision, think and believe is what we will create. Consider how different the world would be if TV and radio programming only broadcast information about the positive aspects of life, instead of all the ills and deviances. These negative thought forms are the major factors in creating the world you see. Think about the world our children and grandchildren will live in. Be discerning, selective and only support people and empowering causes that truly make this world a better place to live. Think about this: Has the campaign, "Say NO to drugs" worked; if not, why not? It can't work because the brain only records the last word …drugs …drugs …drugs. The saying needed to be, "Say "NO" to drugs and Say "YES" to life."

CHAPTER 5

Sharry Edwards

Is Frequency our "New Medicine" or an Ancient Mystery Revealed?

Did we forget to remember? How much trust in ourselves and nature have we abandoned for what we consider more modern, reliable solutions? Ancient herbal remedies that nourish the normal structure and function of the body have been replaced by Pharmacology which creates, in many cases, "side effects" which add accumulative layers of stress and dis-ease.

What is not complete about Mother's Milk that allows a food conglomerate to make statements claiming that canned, artificial products are superior substitutes for a mother's inherent sustenance for her newborn?

What sensory perceptions have we denied when we accept a commercially grown, good looking tomato for those full of flavor and nutrients grown by local farmer or ourselves?

What manipulation of our crops have been forced upon us as we consume grains that have been shown to cause gut and brain permeability that leads to digestive upset, pandemic brain and genetic disorders suffered by the young (ADHD) and old alike (Alzheimer's)?

What caused us to begin to ignore self-healings such prayer, food, meditation, song, dance, potions, music, laying-on-of-hands, incantations, sand paintings, mud baths, blessed water...and turn to strangers who think they have a right to dishonestly report experimental results to convince us to trust them even though their first and foremost goal is financial gain; profit?

When did the goal of better health become the fodder of greed where the goal was to "harvest" our pockets; leaving wellbeing adrift? Many people have begun to believe that the ultimate objective of our modern-day health care system is our entry into an artificial health care scheme that keeps us tethered until we have run out of money or the will to live. Where does the goal of optimal health and wellness fit into the modern business system? How can we move HEALTH to the top of the priority list of our present-day disease management?

It usually takes a well-funded scientific breakthrough or an overwhelming catastrophe to facilitate overall change that actually makes a difference. People are slow to embrace new scientific information because anything fundamentally different from the status quo intimidates them. Although a major disaster forces transformation, people don't always adjust willingly. For a great many people they won't even admit the problem if they have no hope for something different than what is. Along with hope there must be tools and solutions; choices and options for change.

The most profound and permanent way to cause a shift in perception is through affirmative life experience. In an attempt to help shift perceptions concerning health care, I became involved in the creation of a small, highly innovative educational research facility, the Institute of BioAcoustic Biology and Sound Health. Through the years their studies have supported the assertion that ancient architectures and languages contain math codes that support frequency-based cellular regeneration. Through the journey of revisiting lost knowledge using computer technology, a novel paradigm has emerged which uses frequency as a basis for future "medicine" in support of normal homeostasis.

Our bodies are animated through a complex network of nerves that serve as a communication matrix from our brain and spinal cord to every nook and cranny of our bodies. The neural system generates frequencies that move along these pathways. Any self-healing of the body must interact with these "bio-frequencies". Every aspect of this communication network reaches the brain as a measurable frequency; from sound, to thought, to aroma, to light, to touch.... Bottom line, the brain uses frequency to maintain and have dominion over our structure and function.

If we accept that the brain performs in such a fashion, we must advance the notion that the language of the brain is math. So what do all modern and ancient healing modalities have in common; frequencies defined by math; which can be measured, defined, quantified and manipulated to provide understanding and consensus. If we want to combine all healing methods of evaluation and restoration, we could use the common denominator of frequency.

Known as Human BioAcoustics and/or BioAcoustic Biology through Vocal Profiling, the work untaken by the Sound Health staff is being recognized by conventional medical providers. The Duke Encyclopedia of New Medicine has acknowledged that "Vocal Profiling is an innovative biotechnology" while AT&T has announced that bioacoustics is "the medicine of the future".

It has been written that many great thinkers have attempted to decode the mysteries of the universe using math, geometry, music, frequency and architecture. The popularity of the movie *The daVinci Code* and Dan Brown's most recent book, *The Symbol* has sparked our imagination concerning information that has been kept hidden from the populace. While Brown's books hint that architecture contains hidden knowledge, BioAcoustic outcomes provide support indicating that the ancient Templar Cross contains mathematical codes that may initiate cellular reconstruction.

A few sages have even gone so far as to suggest that the ancients somehow imbued our DNA with the knowledge of self-healing and that we only need to remember how our bodies have been innately programmed to rejuvenate. Could we be self-sustaining, carbon based, propagating robots who have forgotten how to connect with our regenerating codes? Are sequestered memories just a part of planned obsolesce as if we are simply a replaceable appliance? Sylvia Franke in her publication, *The Tree of Life and The Holy Grail* explores some of these possibilities.

Providing a mathematical matrix of the bio-frequency field of the body is very important to the future of understanding the body's ability to regenerate. Research from many fields are converging to provide many of the answers concerning Pythagorean harmonic theory and how it can be combined with modern string theory to explain how DNA "strings" can be dominated using frequency. James Genjewski, using an electron microscope, discovered in 2004 that cells emit sound and published the statement that provides a connection between sound and healing, he states that "sounds emitted from cells, if we could decode them, might someday help doctors "hear" disease and diagnose their patients much more quickly and easily". Science can now approach the problem looking for elusive energy pattern that indicate disease/stress that BioAcoustic Biology answered more than a decade ago.

Physician and researcher John Apsley, MD (E), ND, DC, founder of the International College of Regenerative Medicine and a specialist in the rehabilitation and reversal of chronic degenerative illnesses at cellular level, states that the work being done by many institutions help to support the premise of Human BioAcoustics as he states "Ms. Edwards' work defines and demonstrates the unifying field theory that defied Einstein. There will be many who follow the footsteps of frequency-based medicine because this is where the real future of medicine resides." Apsley agrees with many of the physicians who have examined the studies being done and have agreed that using frequency as an intrinsic healing modality, as in singing and toning, is an ancient tool brought forward into the modern era through the computerized protocols of BioAcoustic Biology through individual bio-frequency assessment.

In the near future, bio-frequencies will become as common an indicator of health as taking your temperature or blood pressure when you visit your health care provider. AT&T, several universities plus pharmaceutical giant such as Pfizer and Glaxo/Smith/Cline are now beginning to work with these principles.

Ancient healing practices, combined with modern technology, utilizes the premise that the body can identify and prescribe for itself, using the algorithms of vocalized frequencies to accurately quantify, organize and extrapolate biometric information.

"The list of how Vocal Profiling can be used seems endless and provides an avenue for the integration of energy medicine with the allopathic approach," states Roman Chrucky, MD. Dr. Chrucky credits this innovative approach with predicting his heart attack last year, and for helping his body reverse a diagnosis of prostate cancer. "My experiences with this technique are very real because they have made a difference in my own life, and those of my patients. I'm very happy with this work, and very happy that Sharry has stuck to these ideas in the face of much adversity. In my opinion, she's the doctor's doctor. I send all my perplexing patients to her even though, by definition, what she does is not medicine."

Known as "vocal profiling" the idea of analyzing the frequencies and modulation of a human voice to evaluate emotional, biochemical and structural status of a person is being used by medical facilities and schools; for military applications; in police work for verification purposes; in research studies for issues thought to be incurable; to determine wellness patterns; to relieve the stress of pain; and to determine exposure to toxins and pathogens. From working with the firefighter's union and engineers at ground zero, to assisting physicians in determining the potential cause of health-related mysteries, this novel work is "Star Trek" medicine in the making.

Not only is there dissatisfaction with health care but there is dissatisfaction with our national leadership. Sound Health has created software-based foundational tools for change that support a model for self-responsibility, and health freedom that includes a personality assessment tool with the ability to reveal intention, hidden agendas and deep consciousness ideologies.

A network of people has been organized and trained in these techniques so that a groundswell of people who can practice this new paradigm of health will be available; while leaving the present broken system behind.

Buckminster Fuller said "In order to change something, don't struggle to change the existing model. Create a new model and make the old one obsolete."

No one argues that the present health care system is in crisis, and that people are seeking alternatives. The intention behind the many public software give-a-ways conducted by Sound Health is to create unity in healthcare by providing options and solutions in support of SELF-HEALTH and self-responsibility.

Through the approach of Bioacoustics Biology, we can use the voice to discern the intentions of ourselves and those around us, the motivations of our partners; and the foundation of our sense of self health and wellbeing can be monitored. Would those abilities be of value in the struggle to attain dominion over the intrinsic right to personal health choices?

From birth to death, we use sounds to express our needs and emotions, but there are additional layers of information hidden within the frequencies expressed as language. In modern times we possess only limited conscious awareness of this information for ourselves, and as a means to understand the intentions of others.

BioAcoustic software has been developed that can use the frequencies of the voice to create a matrix of biometric frequency information, from fundamental DNA to the hidden intentions of those who claim to speak for us. Public classes and software are being distributed to help combat some of the urgent present-day healthcare needs: PreVac (pre-vaccination risk factors), Nutritional Consultant, Muscle Management, Allergy Identification, PTSD Prevention, and Parkinson's Recovery, Countervailing the flu seasons and Radiation Exposure, all in the hopes of setting-up a BioAcoustic Center in every community on the planet.

In order to provide predictability and safety, the concepts of math and medicine often act conjointly to quantify, define and model medical practice. Studies conducted at the Institute of BioAcoustic Biology have consistently demonstrated that math can be much more than a measurement tool; math, as frequency, can be the solution to therapeutic predictability and resolution. Imagine a future in which the individual frequency-based biomarkers contained within the voice can be used to keep us and our world healthy and emotionally balanced.

I have often been accused of being too scientific by some, too esoteric by others. In actuality I see myself as a bridge between both fields of inquiry. Many prestigious publications acknowledge that the tenets of BioAcoustic Biology began in a small, impoverished Appalachian community but will ultimately change health care for decades to come. The leading edge research from Sound Health and the Institute of BioAcoustic Biology demonstrates that the voice is a holographic representation of the body that can be used to transform the concepts of math into useful medical models.

Just as there are pathways of compounds called 'chemistry', there are 'mathways' of subtractive frequencies, called 'Sonistry', which can be used to create a numeric biomarker matrix capable, individually and collectively, of being predictive, diagnostic and prescriptive. These may be seen as a type of biofeedback pathways.

To date there is no universally accepted modality that has the potential to assist in the survival of biological, radioactive and pandemic threats; reverse stroke and muscle trauma or support space travel (as frequency-based solutions show the ability to overcome bone loss and muscle atrophy). In many instances, by the time the cause has been identified, it is often too late to provide remediation. Frequency- based medicine has the ability to provide a prompt and corrective direction in person or via the internet.

A project in conjunction with the U.S. Army was undertaken to test the utilization of this emerging technology to explore the potential of using frequency-based biomarkers to identify and quantify Traumatic Brain Injury (TBI) and the associated Post Traumatic Stress Disorder (PTSD).

The implication of the study was the development of a quantitative, mobile, non-invasive model that could identify the damage caused by close proximity acoustic blast injuries and, ultimately, the restitution of normal brain function and emotional stability. The work being pioneered by Sound Health employs numeric biomarker patterns to assess, evaluate and produce outcomes that support optimal biological form and function.

Our brain communicates using the language of math expressed as frequency. As these signals reach the brain, the bio-frequencies are sorted, routed and assigned an interpretation and responsibility. Our brain and our biology are hardwired to respond to these basic principles of math.

Strange, yet profound, BioAcoustic Biology may be able to explain how a physician might instruct a heart patient to "listen to a specific frequency combination [known for its ability to stabilize heart rhythm] and call me in the morning."

The research being conducted by the Institute of BioAcoustic Biology is on the forefront of energy medicine; creating the doorway to our next dimension of health evolution. In addition, the techniques hold promise in answering questions about how our universe was formed, and how our aging and perception of time can be monitored using frequency.

Such a novel protocol utilizes the premise that the body can identify and prescribe for itself, using the algorithms of vocalized frequencies to accurately quantify, organize, and extrapolate biometric information. BioAcoustic Biology is an area of scientific endeavor that is in the process of becoming scientifically established. Visionary leaders will see this novel idea as a prophecy for a new future which can provide conclusions based on measurable outcomes and observation. This emerging paradigm will become part of future medicine as the consistent and efficacious outcomes continue to accrue.

William Crum, former Governor's appointee to the Ohio State Independent Living Council and father of Willie, a Sound Health care client, confirms that BioAcoustic Biology can provide hope for cases in which conventional medicine offers few options. Crum states, "I was a real skeptic at first. BioAcoustics seemed too good to be true. After seeing Willie's progress, however, I believe that Sound Health is on the periphery of the greatest discovery ever made concerning therapy for the human body."

In developing these techniques, The Institute of BioAcoustic Biology has created a dilemma. How can we take this potential to the public when we don't have enough trained practitioners to serve the need?

To survive, the human race NEEDS BioAcoustic Biology. For BioAcoustic inquiry to survive, practitioners, clinicians and trainers are needed. Public and Professional classes are offered each month; many free with accompanying software.

We want to share this information with the public until enough people of vision will recognize the potential of this work, and come forward to be a part of it. It will take vision and sacrifice, and there may be a time when this technology will be challenged by those who desire to maintain the economic power and dominion over our health. However, the technique of using math as a basis of well-being may be the means of restoring our intrinsic right to self-health.

Whoever controls health controls the quality of life. Health is much more precious than wealth. If we can find a way to control our own health, then we have dominion over our evolution. Sound Health has provided the initial steps to explore this pioneering path to New Medicine!

CHAPTER 6

Bradley Bartholomew

Biophotons

There are many theories that associate the natural frequencies in the body to our state of well-being and general health. For instance, in this documentary *The Business of Disease*, several of the contributors have their own unique approach to analyzing these frequencies with a view to diagnosing and curing illness.

Sharry Edwards uses her unique auditory abilities that allow her to 'hear' each person's Signature Sound. She calls her approach Sonoistry where she has identified a basic set of sounds/frequencies that can monitor, predict and manage biological function. Jacob Liberman, on the other hand, is an authority in the field of light and color therapy; Steven Halpern's healing music has helped millions worldwide to experience the blessings and benefits of deep relaxation and inner peace.

What all these theories have in common is this notion that the body produces natural frequencies, which go beyond the standard theories of conventional medicine. Medical professionals are committed to the notion that the ultimate causes of ill health lie in chemical reactions in the body, with the consequence that cures must take the form of drugs that modify or block these chemical reactions. They are committed to this approach mainly because they can 'see' chemical reactions and, more importantly, because there is money to be made in prescribing, manufacturing and selling these drugs; whereas these natural frequencies in the body are often very subtle and cannot be seen and diagnosed in the same way as chemical properties. So the medical profession tends to deny their relevancy to ill-health. There is no money to be made here.

Biophotons are a case in point. These are very weak although extremely coherent electromagnetic waves that are being emitted all the time by the DNA of all living creatures, not just human beings. These are electromagnetic waves in the optical range and so they are essentially visible light and, being electromagnetic waves, they involve frequencies just like the tonal frequencies or musical frequencies or any other form of oscillating phenomena. Because they are actually being emitted by the DNA, they may be considered the primary or base frequencies in the body. At the same time proteins are being synthesized from the DNA, which are the building blocks of all our bodily organs and cells. It is reasonable to expect, therefore, that these frequencies being emitted from the DNA in the form of biophotons are actually capable of transmitting information and data to the proteins. In this way the DNA maintains overall control and regulation of all our bodily functions, and indeed all facets of our life. In this chapter, we will take a closer look at these biophotons, and where better to start than with the man who actually discovered them about four decades ago.

In 1970 Fritz-Albert Popp was a theoretical biophysicist teaching radiology at the University of Marburg in Germany. Radiology involves the interaction of electromagnetic (EM) radiation on biological systems. At that time he was working on two almost identical molecules – benzo[a]pyrene and benzo[e]pyrene. This is organic matter; the former is a lethal carcinogen and the latter is not. There is only a very small difference in their molecular makeup and yet the difference in their toxicity is profound. Popp was observing the different effects of UV light on these molecules.

Popp's experiments were motivated by the findings of a Russian biologist, Alexander Gurwitsch, who in 1923 had proposed that onion roots could communicate with each other using UV light. Gurwitsch had found that onion roots could stimulate the roots of a neighboring plant if they were in a quartz glass pot which allowed UV light to pass through, but not if the pots were made of silicon glass which filtered UV light. As this was the only difference between the two forms of pot, it became apparent to Gurwitsch that the plants must be communicating using ultraviolet light.

Ultraviolet light has a wavelength of about 380nm and a frequency of 10^{15}Hz. If you look at any standard chart for electromagnetic waves, you will see that a wavelength of about 380nm is just outside the range of visible light. This wavelength is shorter than visible light and its frequency is faster. Ultraviolet and visible light are electromagnetic waves the same as all the other waves in the electromagnetic spectrum. These range from radio waves that have a very long wavelength and a comparatively slow frequency through to gamma rays with a very short wavelength and very fast frequency of 10^{20}Hz. The ultraviolet light that Popp used was toward the middle of the electromagnetic spectrum as is visible light.

So when Popp was using UV light on these benzopyrenes, he found that the toxic version, which is found in coal tar and cigarette smoke among other things, absorbed the light and then re-emitted it at a completely different frequency. The other harmless molecule allowed the light to pass through unaltered. The carcinogenic molecule appeared to Popp to be a light 'scrambler.'

So, Popp proceeded to perform the same experiment on other compounds, 37 in all, and he got precisely the same result. He found that he was able to predict which substances were carcinogenic from this scrambling effect they had on UV light. In every case they re-emitted the light at a different frequency.

Those that were carcinogenic substances also absorbed the light at a specific frequency – 380nm in the ultraviolet range.

Popp went in search of an explanation for this and came across the phenomenon called 'photorepair.' You can blast a cell with ultraviolet light to the point that it is almost completely destroyed (including the DNA in the nucleus), and then by simply using light of the same frequency, but of much weaker intensity, the cell can be restored as good as new. In addition to which, Popp knew that this photorepair process is defective in patients with *xeroderma pigmentosum*. These patients actually die of skin cancer as a result of solar damage because their skin has no ability to repair itself.

It was even known that photo-repair works most efficiently at a wavelength of 380nm, the same frequency that these carcinogens were absorbing light and then scrambling it. Obviously there had to be some connection, or at least it appeared so to Popp, who proceeded to write a ground-breaking paper that was published in a prestigious medical journal, where he argued that there must be some kind of light naturally produced by the body that is responsible for photo-repair. Furthermore, external substances must cause cancer by absorbing this natural light and scrambling the frequency so the body loses its repair capabilities.

After this initial discovery Popp and his Ph.D. student, Bernhard Ruth, set about to prove that light was emanating from the human body. His student was a gifted experimental physicist and he constructed a machine along the lines of an X-ray detector that could count photons one at a time. This machine had to be extremely sensitive in order to accurately capture the extremely weak emissions that they assumed would be emanating from the human body. After many experiments using this machine, Dr. Popp exclaimed in a documentary taken in the laboratory at the International Institute of Biophysics:- "We know today that man is essentially a being of light."

By 1976 they were testing cucumber seedlings, and were surprised by the intensity of the photons, or light waves, that were emanating from these seedlings. To rule out the possibility that the intensity of the light was due to the effect of photosynthesis, they next performed the experiment on potato seedlings that had been sprouted in the dark. Their photomultiplier machine registered light coming from these potato seedlings which was even more intense than what they had found in the cucumbers. In addition, they noticed that this light from living organisms was much more coherent than the light from their earlier experiments. A coherent light is one that retains its precise sinusoidal waveform (a mathematical curve of smooth, repetitive oscillation) for longer periods of time. Laser light, for instance, is one of the most coherent forms of light. So when Popp found specifically the coherence of this light, it meant that the light emanating from these living organisms was in the nature of laser light.

Popp developed theories about how light from the food we eat is stored in the body. He knew that when we eat green vegetables like broccoli, it is metabolized into carbon dioxide and water, and he reasoned that the energy from these photons must be distributed over the entire spectrum of electromagnetic frequencies and dissipated in the body. This energy, he reasoned, was the driving force for all molecules. Chemical reactions can occur when electrons are activated by photons of a certain frequency and therefore the appropriate amount of energy. Green vegetables are known to have certain specific beneficial effects on the body so ultimately it is actually the photons stored by green vegetables which are responsible for triggering these effects. This is the forerunner of much theory which is widely accepted today that electromagnetic vibrations from these biophotons are specifically directing chemical reactions and acting as a catalyst to speed up reactions that would be much slower at body temperature of 37°C if unfacilitated by electromagnetic energy.

Popp came to the conclusion that photons (light) control everything in the cell. He found that all the molecules that make up the cell responded to individual frequencies, and that these molecules in turn modulated the frequencies of other processes further down the line. The photons have been likened to the conductor of an orchestra directing all the individual instruments (components in the cell) with his baton. Different frequencies signal all the myriad processes and functions.

These findings by Popp have been the forerunner of a sizeable and ever growing body of research known as Biophotonics or Bioinformatics. For instance, an article *The Real Bioinformatics Revolution: Proteins and Nucleic Acids Singing to One Another?* which was co-authored by Irena Cosic, Professor of Biomedical Engineering, RMIT University, Melbourne, Australia and Dr. Veljko Veljkovic of the Institute of Nuclear Sciences, of Belgrade, Serbia. Hundreds of new chemicals are made by the chemical industry, and these researchers developed a method for predicting whether any of these chemicals may be carcinogenic. Their methods were based on certain electronic properties of the molecules along similar lines to what Popp was doing. It all relates to electromagnetic waves. In addition to determining which chemicals were carcinogenic, they were also able to predict which organic chemical may be mutagenic or toxic, and indeed which organic chemicals may be potentially antibiotic or anticancer agents.

There is so much of conventional genetics and biology that remains unexplained. For instance, how enzymes can recognize their substrates; how antibodies in the immune system can grab onto specific foreign invaders and disarm them; how proteins can 'dock' with different partner proteins, or latch onto specific nucleic acids to control gene expression, to mention but a few.

The best explanation offered by biologists and geneticists is variations on the so-called 'lock and key' model where molecules randomly bump into each other and, in so doing, they find other molecules with complementary shapes that they can lock into, and thus allow biochemical reactions to take place. The process has been likened generally to finding a friend in a very big crowded ballroom in the dark. In every cell there can be hundreds of thousands of molecular pair-wise interactions every second, so the conventional explanation of finding the best fit through random collisions is actually no explanation at all.

Likewise, the explanations of geneticists that segments of DNA are translated and transcribed into proteins is devoid of any specific explanation as to how genetic information actually translates into biological function. The one DNA sequence can encode for several different proteins through multiple splice sites or whatever. Genes and proteins with similar sequences can have totally different functions. Although it is widely accepted that the secondary and tertiary structure of proteins are crucial for their functioning, the basis sequences of amino acids that make up the protein are completely silent as to the how and why of these protein structures. All this information and much more besides must come from some source other than the linear sequence of bases of the DNA molecule. As Dr. Mae-Wan Ho states in her book *The Rainbow and the Worm – The Physics of Organisms*, "The conventional account is also too mechanical, and at odds with the fuzzy picture of atoms and molecules as 'clouds' of probability density in quantum theory."

It is obvious that a mechanical explanation for the molecular interactions in cells is inadequate, and Veljkovic and Cosic have argued that the interactions are actually electromagnetic in nature. Each molecule can send out a unique electromagnetic field that can sense the field of a complementary molecule. They envisage the cellular milieu as a kind of ballroom with all the molecules dancing to the rhythm of these biophotons. The molecules send out specific frequencies of electromagnetic waves which enable them to 'see' and 'hear' each other at a distance. They see each other with optical waves (photons) and hear each other with acoustic waves (phonons). This enables them to interact at a distance and the dance begins. The photons and phonons are capable of exciting the molecules at the atomic level, and this is what is necessary for a chemical reaction to take place.

This molecular resonance is well known in chemistry and something very similar happens with music. When a piano tuner strikes a tuning fork next to a piano, a string, if correctly tuned to the same frequency, will start to sing back to the vibrating tuning fork. When this happens the energy is a two-way street. The waves cause energy to flow from the tuning fork to the piano string, and *vice versa* which is why the vibration lasts much longer when they are resonating at the same frequency. It is also known that molecular resonance is extremely selective for fine tuning. This mutual vibration phenomenon will occur only if there is less than a 1/10,000th variation in resonant frequency.

Cosic analyzed more than 1,000 proteins and over 30 functional groups, and the results showed that proteins with the same biological function share a *single* frequency peak; and by the same token, proteins with different functions have no significant peak frequency in common. Generally she found that the characteristic peak frequency differs for different biological functions. She proposed a Resonant Recognition Model (RRM) of molecular function, and produced a table of specific frequencies for various DNA regulatory sequences and many protein sequences. As a rough estimate she found the maximum and minimum wavelengths of the electromagnetic radiation to be 30,000 and 300 nanometers respectively. In other words the radiation ranges from the very low infrared through the visible to the ultraviolet.

Popp had found these 'biophoton emissions' and recognized that they would provide an ideal communication system amongst the many cells in an organism, but the question still remained as to where this light was actually coming from. One of Popp's students actually suggested the answer to him. A certain chemical, ethidium bromide was known to cause DNA to unwind by insinuating itself between the base pairs of the double helix. The suggestion was to measure the light coming from the DNA after it has been unwound in this way. When Popp tried it, he found that there was a direct correlation between the intensity of the light and the amount the DNA unravelled. The greater the concentration of ethidium bromide, the more the DNA unravelled, and the stronger the intensity of the light. Conversely less ethidium bromide meant less unravelling of the DNA and the light was less intense. This light being emitted from the DNA seemed to include a wide range of frequencies, and these frequencies seemed to be linked to specific functions in the cell. Popp reasoned that the DNA must store light, which would explain why more light was emitted the more it was unravelled.

This also suggested an explanation for the way body tissue, and particularly skin, can repair itself after being cut or scratched. Somehow the injured cells can send a signal to nearby healthy cells to start reproducing more healthy cells to fill in the gap. Once the cut or abrasion has been mended then another signal will tell the neighboring cells to stop reproducing. It was not known how this mechanism actually works. Popp looked at the problem from a holistic perspective and reasoned that there must be one central orchestrator for this process. The weak light emissions from the DNA would be sufficient to orchestrate the coordinated response to body repair and. at the same time, operate in the very small intracellular space (virtually a quantum space) between cells. More intense light would create too much 'noise' at the quantum level and so would no longer be a candidate for the operations that were going on here.

Popp continued his investigations into this light coming from the DNA. He found that different species produced light of varying intensity and frequency. It appeared that the more complex the organism, the fewer were the photons being emitted. For instance simple organisms and plants were emitting light with

100 photons/cm²/sec at a wavelength between 200-800nm. This is a very high frequency EM, well within the visible range. Conversely, humans at this frequency (namely visible light) emit a light that is 90 per cent less intense.

Popp experimented extensively on the light being emitted from humans. He took photon readings from the hands and forehead of one of his assistants, a 27-year old woman in good health, every day for nine months. He found that the biological rhythms at 7, 14, 32, 80 and 270 days, and the emissions from both hands were correlated; which suggested that the biophoton emissions were an essential metabolic process. Similarities in biorhythms were also noted by day or night, week and month, as though the body was somehow resonating with the external world.

Next, Popp tried to find characteristic differences in biophoton emission between those who were healthy and those who were ill. He tested a series of cancer patients, and found that in every case they no longer had those biological rhythms, which his healthy assistant had displayed. He took this to indicate that the lines of internal communication had been scrambled. They had lost their connection with the world almost as if their light was going out. He also found that biophoton emissions from cancer patients lack coherence, and that malignant tumors are emitting photons at an approximately 1,000 percent increase on normal skin. Tumors emit on average 300 photons/cm/minute compared to 22 photons/cm/minute for normal skin. Such a marked increase must have a biological significance. Furthermore, it was found that surface tumors as well as tumors excised during surgery will respond to remedies involving reduced photon emissions. A beneficial agent with reduced photon emissions will not kill the cancerous cells; rather it appears to stimulate the normal cells to overcome the cancerous ones.

At the same time, Popp was developing a theory that these photon emissions were indicating an alternative explanation to

Darwinism for the evolution of the species. It wasn't simply a matter of finding a cure for cancer or *Gestaltbildung*. These emissions seemed to be directing the way living organisms function and evolve. The DNA could be using electromagnetic frequencies at different levels to encode and transfer information. Evolution then was not occurring as a result of random mutations in the DNA (the conventional explanation); rather, the DNA was specifically directing the course of evolution by means of the information that it was able to store and transmit to the various products that are synthesized from the DNA (proteins, hormones, enzymes, neurotransmitters, etc.).

As part of this overall process, Popp came to the conclusion that these biophotons held the key not only to illness, but to what is healthy or unhealthy generally. He started experimenting on foodstuffs.

In one case he compared the light from the eggs of free-range hens to those from factory farms where the hens are crowded into cages. The photons in the former were found to be significantly more coherent than from the latter. This notion of coherence is most significant. Coherent light retains its sinusoidal waveform for much longer periods and is thus able to convey precise information. Light that has lost its coherence has lost its precise shape, and the signal becomes scrambled or even lost altogether. Whatever functions conducive to good health and the production of more coherent light from the free-range hens are simply lost from the eggs of the factory farm hens.

Popp pioneered the process of using biophoton emissions as a tool for measuring the quality of food. He was able to determine that low intensity and high coherence meant healthy food. Whereas, in unhealthy food, the electromagnetic waves are out of sync and there is increased intensity due to overproduction of photons. It seemed that the lower the intensity and the higher the coherence showed how well the organism was communicating at the subatomic level. These days biophoton emission is routinely used in agricultural science to test the quality of foods, and it has wide commercial applications. There are many patents for the use of biophoton emissions for quality control in the food, cosmetics and health industries, as well as general environmental applications.

For instance, biophoton therapy is the application of light to particular areas of the skin for healing purposes. We have already seen Popp's initial insight that these biophotons can actually be responsible for the photorepair phenomenon, and that carcinogenic and toxic substances can actually block the natural repair systems in the cells.

By applying light to the skin at appropriate frequencies, the light is absorbed by the skin's photoreceptors which then can actually travel through the body's nervous system to the brain. These therapeutic frequencies can then regulate our so-called bioenergy which presumably is something akin to our natural life force, and determines our well-being at a fundamental level. If we are experiencing pain, this can also be relieved simply by stimulating certain areas of the body by light with specific frequencies and intensities. Many doctors practice this biophoton therapy, and it is all based on Popp's initial theories that light can affect the electromagnetic oscillations or waves in the body, which in turn can regulate specific enzyme activity. Enzymes which are known to have myriad applications in the chemical reactions in the living cell are of course synthesized from the DNA so it would be natural to expect that the light being emitted from the DNA would be ultimately responsible for all chemical reactions in the functioning of the cell.

Popp wrote extensively about his discoveries and over the years he built up a substantial following from scientists, doctors and others involved in health research. The fundamental premise was that the body's communication system is a complex network of resonance and frequency, which is responsible at a fundamental level for the chemical reactions being studied in conventional medicine, genetics and organic chemistry.

Mainstream medicine has only come to know about biophotons in recent decades thanks to the discoveries of Popp; whereas the chemical reactions in the body have been studied for centuries and, of course, are much easier to work with experimentally. Many groups of scientists have taken up the challenge to specifically study the bodily processes in terms of electromagnetic waves. Together they make up the International Institute of Biophysics which has been specifically created to further this research.

Popp is still coming up with groundbreaking new insights into the potential of this research. For instance, he went on to study the light emissions from several organisms of the same species. One such species was a type of water flea of the genus Daphnia. These interesting little creatures were found to be literally sucking up the light being emitted from each other. He next turned his photomultiplier machine on certain small species of fish and they too seemed to be consuming each other's light emissions. The process seems akin to that of sunflowers, which act like photon vacuum cleaners, seemingly "hovering up" as much solar light as they can possibly get. Even the lowly bacteria, the germs of this world, were found to be swallowing the light from whatever media they were put in. We are all absorbing light from each other like the sunflowers absorb light from the sun. For all living creatures, light seems to be the most essential life-giving commodity of all. Popp then came to the conclusion that all creatures great and small were 'beings of light.'

This opened up the possibility of communication between organisms. Popp realized that these light emissions must have a purpose outside the body. It wasn't just a matter of inter-cellular communication, but also information being sent between organisms. He actually coined the phrase 'photo sucking' for this exchange of light between living beings.

Here was the explanation for the way schools of fish or a swarm of bees or a flock of birds seem to act in perfect unison. They are all linked through light waves, meaning that communication is instantaneous; also, the mysterious homing abilities of birds, bees and fish. Termites that cannot even see can unerringly construct a perfectly symmetrical nest, although working from different directions and compartments. For all these phenomena it has been demonstrated that it is not a matter of simply following habitual trails or familiar scents, nor has it anything to do with the magnetic fields of the Earth. It is as if they are all linked by something akin to invisible rubber bands and, in the case of some migrating creatures, they somehow manage to flock in unison to some place on the other side of the world. Evidently some unseen energy is guiding them and that can only be electromagnetic waves, which can indeed act like invisible rubber bands linking us all.

So this could actually mean that if our own light goes awry in some way, maybe by exposing ourselves to the healthy light of others we could bring about our own return to form. Indeed, there have been experiments that suggest it's possible to transmit death signals to other organisms by means of this light. These are the experiments of V.P. Kaznacheyev and his team who are really taking us into the realm of the paranormal. The team's work is reminiscent of the very early experiments of Russian biologist Alexander Gurwitsch, about onion roots communicating with each other through glass which will not allow UV light to pass, and quartz which will allow in all light. These researchers used cell cultures instead of onion roots that were placed in quartz containers in separate rooms, with the dividing wall containing a window that could be of glass or quartz. The cells in one room were killed by a variety of means – virus infection, toxic irradiation, poisons, etc. – and if the window to the adjoining room was made of quartz that allows the transmission of UV and infrared, then their neighbours would likewise sicken and die. If, however, the window was made of ordinary glass, which is opaque to UV and infrared light, the neighboring cells remained alive and well.

It seems that Kaznacheyev and his colleagues performed over 5,000 experiments of this kind, all in total darkness. They found that in the experiments using quartz, the complementary sickness induced in the neighboring culture occurred within about two to four hours of the mortal peril of the primary culture. It has been suggested then that glass is a suppressor of the 'paranormal channel', although there does not seem to be anything paranormal about it.

Also in 1950, Western researchers used ultraviolet radiation to kill cells kept in darkness, after which they kept these dead cells completely shielded from visible light for 24 hours or more. By this time these cells were clinically dead yet the researchers could revive them by simply radiating them with visible light. Certainly the explanation given by Kaznacheyev and his team in relation to their experiments does not rely on the paranormal. They suggest that every cell emits 'mitogenetic radiation' (as coined by Gurwitsch), which is a weak ultraviolet light. This occurs in a cell's life only twice: when it is born and when it dies. These ultraviolet photons emitted at death are said to contain a virtual state pattern of the condition of the cell at death. When healthy cells are bombarded with these death messages from the dying cells, the death pattern is diffused throughout the healthy culture, thereby pre-empting death of the healthy cells as well. These findings about mitogenetic radiation have been strenuously disputed or denied by main-stream geneticists and biologists, particularly since the time of World War II. According to the conventional approach, there is no such thing as mitogenetic radiation; and even if it does exist, it can have no biological relevance whatsoever. In mainstream biology mitogenetic radiation does indeed come under the heading of the paranormal.

As practiced in traditional Chinese medicine, acupuncture points are a system of meridians, running deep in the tissues of the human body. They are vortices for the channelling of the life force known to the Chinese as *ch'i*. This life force enters the body through these meridians and then flows on into the vital organs. If these pathways or channels become blocked then illness will be the result. Popp was able to reinterpret this theory, which is silent as to the exact nature of the so-called 'life force', in terms of the meridian system representing specific electromagnetic waves (the biophotons) which are transmitted to specific zones in the body.

Popp's theory about acupuncture has been tested by orthopedic surgeon Dr Robert Becker, who developed a special electrode recording device that could roll over the body; and he found that many of these acupuncture points are characterized by a markedly reduced electrical resistance when compared to the surrounding skin. The figures for the reduction in electrical resistance are quite staggering. At the acupuncture meridian points the resistance was found to be 10 Kilo-Ohms (that's 10,000 Ohms) compared to the resistance in the surrounding skin of 3 Mega-Ohms (that's 3,000,000 Ohms). Such a dramatically reduced resistance would indeed enable the most subtle electric currents to pass freely, which would be completely blocked in the adjacent skin areas.

Other researchers have supported this notion that the electrical and optical properties of meridians are different from surrounding tissue; in fact, meridians have been compared with electrical transmission lines. Methods have been developed to actually visualize the radiation emanating from the body using infrared cameras in the range of between 1 – 5 μm (micrometers). A micrometer is a millionth of a meter. This radiation has been described as solitons, which are optical waveguides for the propagation of electromagnetic pulses without losing their coherence and form. They do not spread out during propagation, unlike conventional linear waves. In other words these solitons are capable of transmitting information. It is known that charged solitons propagating along organic molecules, such as DNA, emit electromagnetic radiation of characteristic frequencies; and the existence of coherent electromagnetic fields in living matter is beyond doubt. It is also known that living matter, which has been variously described as nonlinear optical crystals and liquid crystals specifically, supports the propagation of electromagnetic solitons. The electromagnetic field is said to become 'self-focused' which can mean the specific output of the DNA as a result of optical quantum computing.

This is just a small fraction of all the material available about the direct connections between biophotons and our well-being on the one hand, and the direct connection between biophotons and disease on the other. I could cite dozens of research papers that clearly prove that anomalies in the frequencies of these biophotons are directly related to a wide variety of serious diseases, including cancer. And yet the medical profession and mainstream geneticists will flatly deny that this light being emitted from the DNA is in any way connected with disease, or is even worthy of research. These same professionals will admit that they don't know the cure for cancer, for instance, and many other diseases. Yet they remain doggedly committed to research into chemical reactions and the development of drugs because this will assure them the lucrative research grants. It could be said that it is simply not profitable for them to actually find a cure.

CHAPTER 7

Kathryn Rossi

Art, Yoga and Healing

"If I can experience five minutes without pain, I can create a lifetime without pain." Kathryn Rossi

A major injury can create a dramatic paradigm shift away from a usual and expected life to open doors for new, expanding, creative consciousness. I've had two life-changing head injuries, both of which catapulted me into vastly new realities.

My first head injury, at the age of 28, was a slip and fall on wet glazed tile in a parking lot. I broke cervical vertebrae in my neck at C-3. Paralysis from the neck down is the usual result of a C-3 fracture, but I was fortunate and grateful to have eclipsed this outcome. I promised myself if I could experience life without pain I would make my dreams come true, return to school and earn my Ph.D. in Clinical Psychology. It took three and a half years to transcend this brain and body trauma and become pain free. Every day I looked for the absence of pain. I did not want to become so involved and attached to debilitating pain that I would miss enjoying the comfort of no pain. I believed then, as I believe now, that if I can experience five minutes without pain, I can create a lifetime without pain. Incremental successes encouraged me to reach for the next set of possibilities for healing. Chiropractic care and freshwater aerobics were the biggest catalysts for this first healing experience, along with stretching, walking and good nutrition. I tried pharmaceutical medication: pain blockers and anti-inflammatory pills, but found after a few days my mood was minus and dropping and my pain was so intense that these medications were not effective enough to withstand the side effects. I became interested in neuroscience and this injury propelled me into 25 years of study before my next, and hopefully last, injury.

Panama Surfing

In the tropical islands of Northern Panama, at the age of 53, I suffered a second traumatic brain injury while surfing. I am cautious by nature and so this surfing accident happened in a *one-foot tall wave, in one foot deep water, 15 feet from shore*. I caught a small rogue wave that was 10 times more powerful than the waves I had been surfing. I clutched the rails of my surfboard until my hands cramped to get into shore. Once I thought it was safe — being only 15 feet from dry sand — I rolled off my surfboard, panting with all the effort, and sat down. How that small wave picked up my 9 foot 20 pound surfboard and hurled it airborne into the left side of my skull is still a mystery. I saw the surfboard out of my left peripheral vision when it was 18 inches from my head with less than one second before impact.

Time stands still under certain circumstances and this was one of them. I had the presence of mind to understand this surfboard would hit me and I should prepare. I told myself, *"go with it, relax and move with the momentum of the impact."* Had I been in deeper water I would have had time to dive underwater and avoid all impact. Sitting in one foot of water gave me no option other than to take a major hit. What happened next was remarkable and phenomenal dialogues began instantaneously questioning my brain, emotions and neuroscience. Were the scientists right, or wrong in how they think the brain works?
Ouch!

The pain of impact from the surfboard to my head was totally unexpected. I wanted to pass out to get away from this intense pain. A voice shouted inside of me: "PASS OUT AND DIE." What a stunning declaration this is! Anger flew like a rocket into the center of my being. I was angrier in that moment than in my whole previous life combined. Anger saved my life.

Milton H Erickson, MD , was the modern-day father of rehabilitation and therapeutic hypnosis. Erickson's naturalistic principles of utilizing what is around you resonated deeply in my bones from my previous professional training as a Clinical Psychologist. As I looked around my immediate environment for what might help me, Dave Oliver, a gifted yoga teacher appeared. Dave came to Panama to learn to surf. We met at the airport. Generously he offered yoga classes morning and afternoon to anyone who wanted to join. I had never practiced yoga, but after my injury I thought yoga might help me avoid stiffness in my neck and the rest of my body after the severe bonk to my head. Like clockwork, after breakfast and before dinner, I practiced yoga with Dave. Often I was the only person that showed up for yoga class and so Dave made it yoga for Kathryn. He guided me verbally and would also physically adjust my postures. Stretching generally alleviates injury while contraction can cause injury.

The Golden Moment

At the end of each day I experienced a few minutes without pain in my body and head. After a serious injury sometimes a window opens up where you can see your future of how you will be after you recover. A few minutes each day without pain meant I could create a lifetime without pain and would indeed recover from this traumatic brain injury. After five days of practicing yoga with Dave a remarkable thing happened. Standing on the tropical wood yoga deck we watched sea turtles and dolphins in the bay. I turned and said, *"Hey Dave, I think I'm working with the top 10% of my consciousness!"* Dave replied, *"That's actually why people practice yoga."* I took a deep breath and said, *"Really?"* This was a revelation to me that a physical practice could engage my brain and encourage me into higher consciousness. I knew then that yoga would be instrumental in my healing.

Returning home was a cacophony ranging between discordant jumbles and silences. It is very yogic to bring two opposites together to form an entirely new consciousness and sense of the world. It took a year to negotiate the jumbled mess of my memory and emotions to become peaceful again. I had extensive intermediate working memory integration problems and huge migraine headaches. My long-term memory was so good most people thought that I was fine and fully intact. My intermediate memory worked fine during the day, but did not code itself into long-term memory on my cerebral cortex each night. Unfortunately, I was also unable to be creative.

Lessons learned while recovering from breaking my neck were helpful but not enough. I had to mitigate symptoms of headaches, memory loss and sense of myself in the world. I had to rebuild my brain.

What kind of brain do you want to create?

It makes sense that if you have to rebuild your brain, you might as well put some thought into its design. I wanted a brain that resonated with art, truth and beauty, and is nourished by higher consciousness. I wanted to step out of the minutia and daily details of life and reach for the stars! Research psychologist Donald Hebb in 1949 founded a theory that states, "Neurons that fire together wire together." In other words, what you pay attention and focus on will make neurons in your brain become the default "go to" place. My new and improved brain would be strong with the best the world could offer me.

Art as Healing

Intentionally, I focused on art. Art was my meditation where I prayed; and was my deepest focus. Our home has paintings by my dear friend Lee Lawson. Her art simply fascinates me. She paints fine art with luminous brushstrokes, and layers of colors and textures. Light refracts off her work in ever changing patterns throughout the day and night from different viewing angles. I have never seen any of her art the same way twice.

Song of the Sea © by Lee Lawson, Illustration 1

Above the fireplace in our bedroom *Song of the Sea* (see Illustration 1) rises to full consciousness. She sings her song unapologetically, without self-consciousness. She just is. Beside her is a dream jar of hopes, joys and memories she wants ever present. She sings the truth of who she is. I wake up with her and go to sleep with her. Sometimes she *is* me and sometimes she is others. She shows me how to be original and unapologetic for both my genius moments and my foibles. She never was concerned about my serious, debilitating, migraine headaches or the other pains in my body. She only wanted to hear my truest song of highest consciousness. For hours I would lose myself within her song — my song, her prayers — my prayers.

Vision Quest

Thus began my journey mind-melding with art. I spent countless hours curiously looking deep into these numinous canvases wondering over and over again how did Lee Lawson do this? How does she create magic? How can her art hold my attention day after day after day? I wanted to be able to create magic inside of myself but I didn't know how. I believed if I could understand the deeper meaning of her beautiful art, I could learn how to create magic in myself. She would teach me how.

My Mother's Garden © by Lee Lawson, Illustration 2

The most improbable thing happened one day lounging on a deep, white, Stressless chair in my living room. Gazing at *My Mother's Garden*. I could see my brain as the tree trunks and I wanted my neurons to be as strong as the tree arms of the painting. For the first time, I noticed the unusual composition of this painting. Its wholeness makes perfect sense, but when you look at the individual pieces it is a wonder how it comes together. Leaves on her sleeve extend outside the lines. Who ever heard of tree trunks for arms? And, are they really arms? Some tree trunks seem to be coming out of her head. Hidden in the dark side of her kimono is a giant, naked breast subtly peeking through. She is a strong woman and she is growing. Her wide open eyes are in a state of amazement! What amazes her? What amazes me?

I imagined my brain growing strong, tall and sturdy. My neurons could become as strong as tree trunks! Dendrites from these robust neurons could reach incredible lengths. This was my vision quest. If the improbability of this painting can come together as being whole, then the probability of me restructuring my brain could be possible too. I would become what I dreamed of becoming — a woman with a clear, healthy brain. I know this all sounds esoteric, and it is! But somehow this possibility rang true and I spent hours each day with My Mother's Garden, mind-melding with her strength and growth.

A Time for Brain Studies

Several months passed and I was not getting better; in fact, I got worse. An MRI brain scan was ordered. If I had permanent brain damage, then I'd like to know and accept it. The MRI showed two very small lesions. Certainly those lesions were larger months earlier. The insular cortex is involved in the body's sense of space and time and in its subjective emotional experiences, among other things. At the time I was never sure if my feet were underneath me, and negotiating stairs was terrifying. I was not dizzy; I simply didn't know where my body was in space and time. Most people have a fast intuition to know if they are safe in places that they enter. I did not. I engaged internal logic dialogs to intellectually help myself in each situation as to whether or not I was safe. I have great compassion for agoraphobics who have difficulty leaving the house. In my case, I knew my fear of leaving the house would pass as I healed more.

Heartened that my brain problems were few, I discovered the truth. I'd already achieved phenomenal healing and had not yet recognized it. I was ready to take the next step, and that step was yoga.

"When the student is ready, the teacher will appear." Buddhist Proverb

Yoga Training

Six days a week I went to Authentic Yoga Teacher Training. Each day I stayed from 8 to 12 hours. I arrived on time ready to pay attention and I gave it my very best. I did not remember what happened from one day to the next. It was like the movie Groundhog Day repeating the same day over and over again. The physical yoga practice I learned was Asthanga, which has the same sequence of postures each time you practice. This was my litmus test to see if I had a memory that carried from today into tomorrow. Every day, for 30 days, I could not remember the sequence. I had to look around the room for guidance to see what came next.

Learning Sanskrit with Cheryl Oliver was comical. Creating the sounds is like making a party inside your mouth. The shape of your mouth changes with the different letters, as does the position of your tongue. Very few people will know if you're speaking Sanskrit correctly. It's not like trying to learn Spanish where lots of people will know if your pronunciation is correct. In the scheme of life, if I never learned Sanskrit I would not be thought less of. In other words, no one would think I was stupid if I couldn't speak Sanskrit. But the big question was, "Will it work?" From a neuroscience perspective, new learning is invaluable for creating new neuronal pathways and strengthening old ones. My life literally depended on getting my brain to work again. I tried to bring good humor with me each day for every class. There were times it was very hard, but this was my daily and hourly goal.

In conjunction with yoga teacher training Dr. Carlos Santos, a profound Naturopathic Medical Doctor (NMD) and acupuncturist, treated me twice a week. Acupuncture stimulates electrical activity throughout the body, among other things. I could feel sensation of these currents in my brain and how there were blocked places impeding free-flowing electrical activity. With each treatment something good would happen. At times my emotions came out in dramatic ways. Dr. Santos was compassionate and understanding and he never looked at me like I was a crazy lady. The day the blocks opened I gained the freedom I wanted so much. It was extraordinary.

Usually acupuncture does not hurt. On this day pain was severe. It was as if a hammer and chisel were employed to insistently drive and dig through the "rock" that blocked the pathway. On a scale of one to ten, I rated my head pain to be 9.5! The electrical pounding came from both directions, directly at the place where the surfboard hit me. I hoped the "tunnel" would be dug and the current would run free. Acupuncture needles had been placed at these same points for more than a dozen sessions. Knowing this gave me courage to stay with the pain to see if it would transcend into something else. All at once the stunning breakthrough happened. The electrical current in my brain was free to run its circuit without interruption. "Would it last?" I wondered. All afternoon I walked in the desert pondering this question. This pivotal day came 31 days into my yoga teacher training. Neuroscience tells us it takes 30 days to birth a new neuron and another 60 days for it to make connections throughout the brain. I had entered the kindergarten of my healing and was deeply proud. From that day forward my memory began to work and my headaches only returned if I was under stress. Much to my surprise, most of what I learned the previous 30 days had actually encoded in my long-term memory. When I use patience, kindness and compassion with myself, I am able to access what I learned.

Art, yoga, acupuncture, diet and exercise were the catalysts for healing from my surfing accident. Understanding the creative process was vital to managing my time and emotions.

CHAPTER 8

Ernest Rossi

Creating New Consciousness in Everyday Life:

Stroke Recovery via Healing Dreams

I dreamt that I was brutishly clubbed on the head in my sleep. I felt heavy and unable to move out of a cramped fetal position in the nightmarish darkness. I wanted to groan but could not. I did not know whether I was asleep or awake. But I must have opened one eye at least momentarily to glance at the dim, luminous glow of a clock by my bed that registered about 2:30 a.m.

I awakened again at 4:30 a.m. with a strange sluggishness, stiffness and awkwardness of movement. I could hardly roll out of bed. I thought I was suffering from a sudden attack of arthritis or post-polio syndrome. I staggered to the medicine cabinet to try out some new anti-inflammatory medication my primary physician had given me a few days before. I wanted to record the exact time I took the medicine to see how long it took to give me relief. There was no paper handy so I tried to write "4:30" on the medicine package. But something was radically wrong with my writing; it was incredibly tiny and the numbers were written on top of each other! I was uncoordinated trying to take a shower and almost fell. It was a struggle to dress; my right leg could not find its way properly into my trousers. It wasn't until my wife awakened about two hours later that I realized I had badly slurred speech. A quick check of my face in the mirror revealed the truth: the right side of my face was pulled down completely out of its normal symmetry. I now understood - I had experienced a stroke. My wife, Kathryn, called the doctor and rushed me to the hospital.

The music player in our van automatically turned on my favorite contemporary composer, Kitaro. One passage of the music played a haunting drumbeat reminiscent of American Indian music. Suddenly I was seized with a paroxysm of hot tears as I glanced over the pristine countryside of San Louis Obispo through which we were now driving on the way to the hospital. I imagined I was experiencing the truth of the deep tragedy of the American Indian Nations with what seemed to be a profound clarity – a cleansing of perception. Did not anyone else recognize the truth of this exquisite tragedy of the American Indians? Why wasn't something more being done to correct it?

I saw the mortified fear in my wife's face – she had never seen me crying that way. She thought I was crying about myself and tried to reassure me. I had great difficulty with my slurred speech to explain the tragedy of American Indian Nations. I saw her growing alarm as she thought I was surely going daft. I now realized I might be experiencing "affect labiality," rapid shifts in outward expression, which is typical in stroke. I tried to calm down and smile to reassure her but all that came out was a strange, strangled laughing along with the tears that I still could not control.

The music of Kitaro continues to move me to a mystical sense of hyper-reality even today, years after that fateful ride. It is the kernel of a personality change that is still taking place within me as I carefully cultivate a greater accessibility and expression of my emotions, which my wife now greatly enjoys. Here is a partial record of a few dreams of recovery I had during this period that illustrate a new neuroscience view of our natural healing abilities in everyday life. ,

It is rather surprising for most of us, to learn that the ordinary aspects of everyday life such as waking, sleeping, dreaming, eating, work, play, relaxation, memory, learning, stress, conflict, health and illness are all associated with uniquely individual patterns of gene expression that scientists now call "epigenetics." Many of our genes are active players responding adaptively, cooperatively and creatively to the cues, contingencies and emergencies of our ever-changing daily experience.

Creatively Replaying Mind-Gene Communication in the Dramas of Our Dreams

During the third week of my rehabilitation, a neurologist filling out a routine medical form asked me if my stroke has resulted in a loss of physical strength so that I can no longer do my job. I grimly grin at him, square my shoulders a bit, and humorously respond with my stroke-slurred speech, "Well, I'm not exhashly (slur for exactly) an iron foundry worker you know." That night I had this dream.

A huge Paul Bunyan-type man in the hellish glow of an iron foundry is using gigantic iron pliers and tongs to manipulate small metal objects. He is going to teach me how to do it skillfully. I am experiencing great awe that he notices me and I feel very grateful about the prospect of his help.

I view this dream figure to be analogous to my occupational therapist that is assessing and facilitating recovery of my damaged hand-eye and muscle coordination by giving me many tasks involving puzzles, picking up small metal objects with tweezers, etc. I tell him this dream and explain my psychogenomic perspective: Paul Bunyan is a metaphor of an inner implicit healing process operating via *activity*-dependent gene expression that is turning on *activity*-dependent brain plasticity (the growth of new synapses and neurons) that hopefully are now being *behaviorally activated* by all this occupational therapy to repair my brain. He has never heard of this new neuroscience view of rehabilitation but I assure him that my new book is coming out soon so he can read about it. I'm just too exhausted mentally and physically to try to explain it all right now.

As I continue to emotionally replay this dream in my active imagination throughout the day, the Paul Bunyan figure becomes somewhat evocative of Mr. Spock of Star Trek fame. But he is of Chinese blood, red-orange with a thunderous body stretching from the center of the earth to the sky. He has huge massive muscles and an impassive face. He does not speak and he hardly notices me but I am fascinated with the possibility that he actually is a genial gene genie ready, available and fully capable of firing the sources of life should he be called.

Ok, so I'm calling, now! After a week or so of watching him do nothing but stand silently poised with his huge iron tools, Mr. Spock finally becomes activated in my imagination. One morning I awaken with grateful tears when I see him pounding a huge, glowing gold ingot on a mighty anvil with flashing lightning leaping about with every stroke. I gain reassurance as I witness his continuous methodical pounding whenever I call him forth in my creative imagination.

On one level this is an awesome experience – a drama that I feel is deeply healing. Simultaneously, on another level, I recognize with calm objectivity that *this positive emotion is good for me, so I make an active effort to replay it with curiosity, fascination and focused attention as long as I can. This inner drama wherein I am both healer and healed suggests to me that I am experiencing several levels of consciousness within my dreams.* Does this emotionally heightened state of consciousness and imagination in my healing dream mean that my rehabilitation will be facilitated by my being *actively and intensely engaged in the real and imaginative replay of mental exercises,* like manipulating the tongs as illustrated by the Paul Bunyan/Spock figure?

Neuroscience research is now documenting how facilitating gene expression and *brain plasticity* via novel and fascinating *activity-dependent emotional experiences* is a basic mechanism of mind-molecular communication and healing that makes rehabilitation possible.

Patients with severe trauma resulting in loss or paralysis of sensory-motor functions due to physical injury, cardiovascular accidents, and extreme psychological trauma and chronic stress, for example, can recover their abilities via occupational therapy and counseling that works primarily by *activating their behavior, cognition and constructive attitudes.* Until recently this mind-molecular-genomic mechanism of rehabilitative healing by behavioral activation was not understood. *The new neuroscience view is that cognition and behavioral action initiates activity-dependent gene expression. This activity-dependent gene expression initiates healing by the generation of proteins that facilitate brain plasticity and stem cell differentiation into new tissues that can be initiated within minutes and continue for the hours, days, weeks and even years required for full recovery.*

A Dream of Numinous Beauty and Clarity

During the 4th week of rehabilitation I dream:

I enjoy the numinous beauty and wonderment of looking through a new clear crystal cover on our swim spa, seeing the delightful light blue, clean water in the sparkling sunlight.

We actually don't have such a new crystal cover over our swim spa but evidently this dream is a metaphor for some sunlight of clarity coming into the waters of my brain. A battery of psychological tests administered at this time tells the story of my mental status in a stark manner. The good news is that my *abstract reasoning* is still at the 99th percentile level and my capacity for *mental organization* is at the 97th percentile. The bad news is that I am way below normal in *perception and discrimination* at the 45th percentile level and, even worse, my *short-term memory* is down to the 37th percentile.

I spend many afternoons sitting entranced in the sunlight gazing into the clear crystal water of our swim spa with a deep spiritual hunger to drink it all in somehow to assuage my still stunned brain. For the longest time it seems, I find myself struggling to recall the words of the poem *Vacillation,* by Yeats, which I once knew so well:

My fiftieth year has come and gone,
I sat, a solitary man,
In a crowded London shop,
An open book and empty cup
On the marble table-top.
While on the shop and street I gazed
My body of a sudden blazed;
And twenty minutes more or less
It seemed, so great my happiness,
That I was blessed and could bless

As I repeatedly replay this dream in active imagination while struggling to recall wisps of poetry throughout the day for many days, it finally dawns on me that my hunger and preoccupation with the numinous experience of crystal clarity may be an example of what I call the "novelty-numinosum-neurogenesis effect." *The heightened creative psychological experience of numinous beauty, wonderment, and crystal clarity may correspond to the activation of gene expression and brain plasticity to facilitate the healing* of my *perception and discrimination,* which is way below par at the 45th percentile level. I muse over the similarity of the three psychological qualities characteristic of the numinosum (*fascination, mysteriousness, & tremendousness*) in spiritual development described by Rudolph Otto in his book *The Idea of the Holy* and the three facets of *novelty, environmental enrichment and physical exercise* that neuroscience now finds characteristic of the creation of new consciousness via activity-dependent gene expression and brain plasticity to build a better brain in everyday life.

After replaying the numinous beauty of this dream for several weeks, I have a particularly vivid experience of it; an epiphany of sorts, while listening to a live performance of The Russian National Orchestra's rendition of Mussorgsky's *Pictures at an Exhibition*. The program notes quote Mussorgsky's description of his creative fervor while composing this piece: "Ideas, melodies come to me of their own accord ... I gorge and overeat myself. I can hardly manage to put it all down on paper fast enough." Likewise, while listening to this performance, I have a similar experience by recognizing how music, art, poetry, philosophy, and science all come together as one in a new theory of aesthetics: *the numinous experience of beauty could generate gene expression, neurogenesis, and the actual reconstruction of the brain during creative moments described by John Keats as the equivalence of beauty and truth.*

A Dream of Recovery: Creating New Consciousness for Healing

After one year of rehabilitation I have this dream:

I was a mental patient in a gray, barren and dark mental institution. I walk along the main hall with a huge, disheveled man who is a mental patient and a friend of mine. I notice that my sensations are sharp, my perceptions are vibrant, and my mind is clear. No one in the hospital seems aware that I have recovered – I feel that I am well now. On a stairway up to the left is a column of ascending women patients and a dear, sad little girl patient (who reminds me of Anne Frank). I playfully toss her a pink rubber ball to try to cheer her up. On another stairway up on the right side is the office of the medical superintendent of the mental hospital. A nun standing outside his office confides to me that the medical superintendent has an interesting but little known personal history. It seems that he too was mentally ill but he was able to keep his illness under control with his sensible and rational attitude. In fact, all who knew this medical superintendent had a deep love and respect for him because of his humble and helpful attitude to everyone. At that point I turn to my disheveled friend and tell him in a happy voice, "My mind is clear now and I am well! The doctors are going to let me go home now." In this dream I did feel a wonderful clarity that I actually lost for a while after my stroke. My friend turns to me and replies, "Well, of course they are going to let you go. You were able to explain yourself to them clearly so that they could understand who you are." The sad implication of his words was that he and the other patients would have to remain in the hospital diagnosed as mentally ill because they could not explain themselves.

I believe this dream set the feeling tone of my 70th birthday. My basic feeling is gratitude for my recovery, my remarkable luck of living with such a wonderful wife, and my returning mental faculties. My wife tells me that she has noticed over the past few weeks I really am acting clear with full recovery from my stroke. She is almost completely right in this. A recent retest documents that after 15 months of rehabilitation, both of my major stroke-induced deficits improved dramatically: my *perception and discrimination* improved to the 90th percentile from the 45th; and my *short-term memory* improved to the 66th percentile from the 37th.

In sum, these real-life healing experiences of dreams and imagination contain the seeds of a new theory of aesthetics, creativity, and science that reifies Keats' poetic and philosophical conundrum, *"Beauty is truth, truth beauty, – that is all ye know on earth, and all ye need to know."* If beauty and truth are both numinous experiences that activate gene expression and brain plasticity, then becoming actively self-engaged with numinous experiences of beauty can actually reconstruct our physical brain to generate new experiences of truth and vice versa.

We normally outgrow many symptoms of stress, trauma and post traumatic problems (PTSD). Further, we can actually learn to facilitate our own natural healing process of mind-gene communication by heightening our consciousness in everyday life with what I call "the Novelty-Numinosum-Neurogenesis Effect (NNNE)." A simple passive exposure to beauty and truth may not be enough, however. *We need to deeply experience the genuine activity of creating new consciousness in everyday life by heightening our personal motivation to turn on our healing genes with the NNNE!*

This leads me to believe that the natural basis of most psychological, spiritual and holistic healing practices such as dreaming, drama, imagination, therapeutic hypnosis, meditation, yoga, etc. actually take place by self-stimulating the activation of our gene expression, stem cells, brain plasticity and immune system. At best, this is how we can improve our culture of cultivating self-healing consciousness with education in the humanities as well as inspiring stories in biographies, novels, movies, documentaries, narratives and public media of all sorts.

CHAPTER 9

Amit Goswami, Ph.D.

How Quantum Activism Can Evolve Civilization

Civilization crucially depends on our values; love, beauty, justice, truth, goodness – this kind of thing. Without them, without human beings striving to love or seek justice or discover truth, there is no civilization. This is what is happening with today's prevalent world view of scientific materialism—everything is matter.

Scientific materialism – the idea that everything is matter, everything is elementary particles at the base level—gives us a mechanical picture of ourselves. Matter cannot process meaning or values. Your body's elementary particles have no sense of what love is, or beauty, or justice, so obviously then if elementary particle interactions govern whatever you do and what you are about, you would be mechanical and your doing would be machine-like. Meaning and values require more than the symbol-processing capacity of a mechanical computer.

Even Darwinian's "survival of the fittest" theory and the idea that "somehow meaning and higher values have survival value and, therefore, when they arise in the genes of biological beings by chance, nature selects them" do not work. How can these attributes of processing meaning and values arise in genes when matter cannot even process them?

Face it! If we were mechanical and material, we just couldn't have these noble values within. It just doesn't work that way. So let's recognize. That the scientists/purveyors of scientific materialism are preaching an inadequate world view which doesn't work for a human being. And even so, their influence has been enormous because they teach this stuff from first grade to our elementary school children where basically nobody dares to challenge the idea that the universe is made up of elementary particles.

So there you have it. Values are denigrated. Everybody's confused about values. Are they real or are they just imagination? You have heard Republican politicians denigrate Democratic values and Democratic politicians denigrate Republican values. Why is that? Because nobody knows if values are imperative in view of scientific materialism.

And so our civilization is going down the drain – literally. If you don't believe it, just look around you. How to save it? Fortunately, the paradigm is shifting. Scientific materialism is incomplete philosophy. It's very clear. Quantum physics makes it super clear and gives us paradoxes that scientific materialism – the idea that everything is matter – just cannot address. So we have to change our world view and instead base it on the primacy of consciousness. When we do that, several things happen.

One is that we can include the whole spectrum of human experiences—sensing (matter), feeling (vital energies), thinking (meaning) and intuiting (archetypal values, love etc.). Because quantum physics says "objects are possibilities". Objects are possibilities for consciousness to choose from. Consciousness is the ground level of being. So if that is the case, then one can easily see that consciousness holds four worlds of possibilities: not only the physical/material world but also the vital world from which our feelings come; the mental world from which our thinkings (about meaning) come; and also the archetypal world from which our intuitions come.

So, when we introduce these values into the very basic structure of our science, I think we can understand these four aspects of value processing pretty quickly and remove all value confusion.

In this way, I think the main gift of quantum activism - the idea that we must use quantum physics to guide how we should live, not the archaic Newtonian old physics - is going to be literally saving civilization.

I agree that when you first encounter the phrase 'Quantum activism' and also the title of my book, "How Quantum Activism

Can Save Civilization", it may disturb you. Many people have told me "Why such a grandiose title for a book?" But actually it is quite appropriate. That's why I agreed with the title. The title was not my first choice but I thought the publisher's choice was better, because it's literally true. Quantum activism can save our civilization because quantum activism says that we have to transform ourselves and our societies from value neutral to value positive. We have to rediscover the values I've mentioned and learn to live them. And that's what transformation is all about. Whoever is aware of the new worldview, for them values become imperative once again (as the philosopher Immanuel Kant envisioned). Society has to do it and we personally have to do it.

THE CONCEPT OF "CONSCIOUSNESS"

What is consciousness? I often begin my workshops on consciousness with this question. And it's really quite amusing how many people don't really have any idea of what consciousness is. Eventually, somebody will say 'well, awareness'. That's the closest that they can come to defining consciousness. But, of course, consciousness is more than awareness. Awareness is a very important aspect of consciousness, which is the most direct that we experience. We experience ourselves as "I"s separate from the world of objects. The subject "I" of awareness is a basic characteristic of consciousness, and probably the most obvious and self-evident one. But there are other characteristics too when you think about it.

Existence, for example. Nobody has to tell me or you that you exist. Why? Because you are conscious. That's such a precious thing that completely lacks in a rock or a piece of wood. A rock exists objectively only as possibility; it manifests only when a conscious being experiences it. The Hindu tradition gives us another characteristic which also is quite apropos, and scientists are rediscovering that characteristic, which is this: we are happy when we experience the facsimile of wholeness; so happiness (Hindus call it by the Sanskrit word ananda) is a characteristic of consciousness.

Happiness has to be distinguished from pleasure. Happiness is wholeness, whereas pleasure can lead to separateness, too.

Pleasure is completely programmed in our brain as a brain circuit. But when you are truly happy, you will notice that there is wholeness. Somehow you and your environment have become one and that's why you are happy. There is no seam, no boundary. So this boundary-less existence is what we mean by consciousness as the ground level of being.

Once in a while we fall into that experience of wholeness. Once in a while we have wholeness anyway – when we sleep. We don't have to do anything, we just sleep. And we become one with the entire universe. Deep sleep is a person's unconscious state but nevertheless when you wake up to awareness, you feel that you are happy. Anybody who has slept well knows it. So in this way, those are the three basic attributes of consciousness: existence, awareness, happiness.

Quantum physics is giving us a fourth one—the idea of downward causation, the capacity of choosing from quantum possibilities of objects and manifesting them. Consciousness chooses and objects transform from possibility into actual events of experience. So this choice, downward causation, is a fundamental characteristic of consciousness.

HOW WE CREATE OUR OWN REALITY AND COLLECTIVE REALITY

Now this one is a very confusing idea, how we create our own reality. Several things need to be said. First of all, there is the consensus reality. How can we possibly create a reality which other people are experiencing too? Obviously, we are not saying that I am the head honcho and everybody else is just a figment of my imagination so I create their reality too. That's absurd. So - first of all, we've got to get very clear on that. Consensus world is the world of matter. We experience it external to us. In the macroscopic world of matter that we experience, quantum effects are so subdued that it's virtually impossible with naked eyes to see quantum movement. And therefore, we think – we get deceived into thinking -- that the macro world is ever present, independent of our looking, independent of downward causation.

And therefore, the macro world experience can be shared. If there is no discernible quantum movement between your choice and my choice, the object is not changing much at all, and therefore both of us can experience it the same way. In this way, we experience a consensus world.

So the consensus world obviously is not the place where we choose our own reality in any discernible way. Where is the discernible signature of our choice then? Well, it is in the inside of our psyche – inside our consciousness where we experience feelings, where we experience thinking and where we experience intuition. Those are the places where we create our own reality. We don't necessarily think what other people tell us they are thinking at any given time. Of course, other people tell us a lot of things that we think. And the majority of our thinking, no question, is guided by other people's thinking. But we CAN do better than think other people's thinking. When we have done that – creative thinking – then we can say 'I create my own reality'.

So, it's a little bit more subtle. Some people may think that "Well, I create my own reality and therefore I can do anything". Somebody, in fact, gave a recipe: intend what you want to create and wait. Things are attracted to you, they will come. But it's not like that.

Of course, creatively choosing your reality may sometimes happen spontaneously, but to get the hang of it, you have to understand what the creative process is. When you recognize what the creative process is, then you realize 'Well, it's not just waiting and creation coming to you because you intended something'. It's more than that. You have to go through a process which involves a considerable amount of doing as well as waiting. I call the process 'do-be-do-be-do'. So it's a little bit more complicated than popularly understood.

BELIEFS, SYSTEMS AND CHANGING OF PERCEPTIONS ALONG WITH PERCEPTION FILTERS

A good question is how to change belief systems. What impact do our belief systems have about what we choose and create? First of all, we have to have a belief system that is flexible. And this is a subtle thing. That doesn't mean that we don't have convictions. I can have strong convictions, but in a flexible way. I keep an open mind about the validity of my convictions.

Do I know love? If you think about it, you'll realize very soon that no, you may have convictions that you love your partner, and that you have loving parents, and that you love your children but do you know love? Can you love anybody? Can you love unconditionally? These questions come immediately to mind and you realize, no – like that Joni Mitchell song lyric – "I don't really know love at all".

And when you realize that, you develop a little bit of an open mind about love. And that open mind is the basis to creativity – that open mind is the basis to creating your own reality because you should know that "I really don't know the fruit of my intention". Then you have to investigate following the creative process. Then when you discover it, you live it and manifest it in your being.

This whole idea is extremely important to help Americans in particular to understand things like quantum activism. A quantum activist is one who is aware that, although he or she knows something about love, does not know everything, but keeps an open mind. The quantum activist has the power to say 'no' to conditioning, and taking actions based on habitual belief systems. This then opens the path to more creative thinking and changing one's perception filters and belief systems.

IS MOST OF OUR LIFE LIVED AS A REPETITION OF MEMORIES AND CONDITIONING?

The great psychologist Carl Rogers had a phrase: on becoming a person. He says – and I agree – that one doesn't become a person until one has chosen something that is totally new. "This is my thought", "this is my feeling", "this is my intuition", "this is my creative discovery to live my life". When you can speak like that, then you have become a person.

It was not that hard to do in a previous era, Americans did that fairly routinely; individualism prevailed. But now, in our materialist society, there's too much tendency for behaving in a programmed manner, for being politically correct, for following other people's thinking. Of course, societies function in an orderly fashion when nothing changes; that's conservatism. That tendency of "don't change anything" is very strong culturally.

The word 'conservative' is very confusing. We don't want to conserve the existing way; the existing conceptual lens that we analyze our ideals with; environment changes, worldview changes. What you want to conserve are the ideals themselves, the values. But usually 'conservative' means that you don't like change, period. Or you want the "good old days" back. You want the 'same old, same old. And "new world" or liberalism means you want all kinds of changes that give you pleasure, although they may not be the most desirable changes for saving the values. So, there again is huge confusion. Confusion goes away when we recognize that changes are essential because the situation changes. Human history has amply illustrated that environment and things change sometimes very much, and that demands new action.

For example, right now there is so much change in our economic, political, and climate conditions that we call it a crisis situation. How can we operate with the same old principles of analysis because those principles were never applied to this new situation. We have to discover new ways of handling this new situation.

Einstein used to say that you can never solve a problem at the level the problem was created. So we've got to go beyond the level that the problem was created. And this is where creativity comes in. Ultimately, creativity is an act of non-local consciousness. What that means is that there is interconnectivity: We are interconnected at the base level of our nonlocal consciousness. Until we discover that, we really cannot live these values. These values are not just words.

When you say 'love', it may or may not mean anything to you really, until you have tried to love someone. You've got to love someone beyond sexuality, beyond just a conventional, socially defined relationship. To really love someone you have to ask questions like: "Can I sacrifice for this person," or "can I love this person unconditionally?" meaning that 'can I accept this person exactly the way he or she is, not the way I want him or her to be?"

So when we inquire in this way, only then do we realize how important it is to recognize the value of creativity; to discover how to live the values we cherish.

PEOPLE WANT EVERYONE ELSE TO CHANGE BUT THEMSELVES

People want others to change, but not themselves; that's the goal of usual activism. Quantum activism from the get go declares that doesn't work simply because the movement of consciousness is not designed to be like that; it is designed to further human evolution.

So, each of us has to ask: "Am I going to go with the evolution of consciousness toward better embodiment of values in myself and in society? Or am I going to be detached from it? Or am I going to live a conditioned life of pleasure (liberals) or maintain status quo (conservatives)?" But face it! You cannot live a life totally of pleasure. Pleasure invariably is followed by pain because those pain circuits are also part of the brain. And the status quo about old religious values is just talking about them, not walking your talk. Talk is cheap.

So if you want to live in a conditioned way, life is never going to be happy or satisfying. Sure, you can hide pain by some pleasures, or by talking lofty things, and that works to a certain extent. But eventually what lacks – and you can discover it very easily – is satisfaction. Your life just tends to become more and more depressed. Depression is lack of satisfaction. You bring satisfaction in life by processing new meaning, by becoming creative, by embodying values. Do that and you'll find your life has satisfaction.

HYPERACTIVITY AND SLOWING DOWN

Today, because of many reasons – one of them being technology of television, telephone, etcetera - we have an epidemic of hyperactive people. We use the 'computer' aspect of our design too much. And what happens then is we become hyperactive. The brain is always throwing out information at us and we process it in our consciousness, giving meaning to it with our mind. And that just makes the brain and the mind go, go, go all the time.

If 'mind' is always going then that is a problem with meditation. We cannot meditate. We have lost the capacity. Why? Because the brain and mind are so hyperactive. How does a society become so hyperactive? Aside from the technology aspect I've already mentioned, another reason is food and nutrition.

The current American culture is so centered on food items that make them hyperactive. Take foods which are heavily concentrated in protein. What is the function of protein? Just think about it. Protein is absolutely essential for our functioning. Without protein we cannot function. But only about 15 to 20 percent of our total food intake needs to be protein; that's all the body needs. If you have excess protein what will happen? The body will always want to work, because proteins are functional agents of the body. You cannot have too much protein and say "I'll be inactive, I'll not do anything." It's just not possible.

People sometimes identify affluence with eating protein. How much protein you eat decides how rich you are. When everybody's concept is shaped like that, they eat as much beef or other meats as they can. But look at the society then because everybody will be hyperactive with that kind of mindset. Add to this the consumption of too many sugar and carbohydrate-rich foods.

When you have a hyperactive mind, you cannot meditate. You cannot slow down enough to meditate. Meditation becomes very boring. And so then you say "Well, I'm not good at it" or "I don't need to meditate." And then you might even become an activist, try to support meditation for others, but you hide the fact that you can't meditate and you don't meditate.

WHAT MEDITATION ACTUALLY IS

What is meditation and what does it achieve? Meditation is the antidote to hyperactivity. So the ability to meditate means only one thing: the ability to pay attention. And really, nobody should give up after a few times of frustration with meditation. If you don't give up, what you'll find is that you can concentrate a little bit better each time. The mistake we make – sometimes the teachers themselves - is to set a time limit. Like TM (Transcendental Meditation) says, do it for 20 minutes but 20 minutes is too long in the beginning. And twenty minutes twice a day is an impossible commitment for most modern people to get into.

So initially, start with one or two minutes. See if you can sit comfortably for just one or two minutes without thinking too much. That capacity, that practice for just one or two minutes a day for a few days will bring the capacity to meditate for five minutes. And then after doing meditation for five minutes for a while, you jump to maybe something like 15 minutes.

I agree that eventually meditation should be 15 to 20 minutes, where you just attentively think on one word in concentration/meditation—it won't be boring. Your mind has slowed down. Then the gap between thoughts will increase and you will be amazed.

One day you will really have this thought – I guarantee it – that "I didn't think anything for a time". Of course, right after you have that thought, you have thought something. But before that, there was a time when you really did not think anything, and you are very aware of it. That's what you're looking for. When that gap becomes solid, when that becomes established, then we are meditators. We are now making room for creativity. Why? Because creativity is a combination of doing and being--do be do be do--alternating between doing and being.

Meditation teaches you how to be, how to relax, how to not think, how to not do. Without meditation, we never can keep up with this constant chattering of our mechanism, the brain.

CHAKRAS AND DISEASE

I'll be a little technical. There are points in the body where we experience vital energies—feelings--the most. These are called the chakra points. Once known only in Eastern philosophy, chakras are now popular everywhere because they suggest common aspects of human experience. These chakras are connected with the biological functions of our organs.

For example, the three low chakras are connected to the reproduction organs and maintenance of the body, and the feelings we have at these points are associated with those biological functions.

But then there are the higher chakras. That's when things become interesting because the higher chakras are connected with feelings of higher functioning in us, higher than survival necessities.

Many physical and mental illnesses come from the suppression of vital energy in the higher chakras. For example, depression comes from suppression of energy in the crown chakra, the chakra having to do with the neocortex. If we are not satisfying our urge to investigate or explore mental meaning – new meaning – then more and more we become dissatisfied with life.

If we are always confused, that's when we block energy in the third eye, the brow chakra. Confusion brings in an enormous sense of unease and anything can happen to the body. People become neurotic as a result with no mental clarity at all.

Throat chakra, associated with feelings of expression, is very important. If we block energy there, then we cannot express anymore. We lead a sort of 'nincompoop' kind of life; very unsatisfactory.

The heart chakra signifies love, romantic love especially. But if heart energy is suppressed – romantic love – the associated organ, the immune system malfunctions. If the immune system functioning is blocked, surely abnormal cells will not be killed off but will become malignant, cancer. So you can even contract cancer.

So in this way, chakra psychology is teaching us a whole lot about how we contract illness and disease.

CHAKRAS AND CREATIVITY

The demand of conscious evolution is to manifest the archetypal values in our lives. To that end we not only need to work with mental creativity but also with creativity in the vital energy dimension. How? For a starter, by keeping the chakras unblocked. Second, by practicing 'do-be-do-be-do' in the feeling dimension. There are vital energy practices—Tai chi, Paranayama—that tend to slow down our organ functioning, increasing the gap between feelings and allowing unconscious proliferation of quantum possibilities in those gaps. If you have more possibilities to choose from, and this is true of both meaning and feeling, your chance of discovering a creative insight to your search will be greater. This is where we humans are more creative than computing machines. Machines operate only at one level. We have the ability to operate at two levels—unconscious and conscious.

When we unblock the chakras, we clean up the unconscious dimensions of feeling. When we allow conflicts in the conscious without suppressing them, we clean out the unconscious mind. Being consciously aware of conflicts in our lives, and allowing them to play out by resolving them with reason, we allow quantum possibilities to proliferate in both thought and feeling. This allows us to be ever more creative.

MAKING BRAIN CIRCUITS OF POSITIVE EMOTIONS

Creative insights are discontinuous quantum leaps to the supramental land of our archetypes. Once we have them, we manifest them in the form of brain circuits for positive emotions. These brain circuits help us to balance the negative, emotional and instinctual brain circuits. This is when transformation takes place in our behavior.

Quantum activism then uses the quantum principles — downward causation, nonlocality, discontinuous quantum leaps - to transform us so civilization can evolve.

CHAPTER 10

Jacob Liberman, O.D., Ph.D., D.Sc. (Hon.)

Divine Guidance

There are only two ways to live your life. One is as though nothing is a miracle. The other is as though everything is a miracle -- **Albert Einstein**

Throughout history human beings have yearned for a higher source of wisdom and knowledge. Ancient indigenous peoples sought guidance from nature, spirits and the cosmos through human intermediaries. These intermediaries were the shamans, oracles and prophets who carried messages between the spiritual and earthly realms. Their messages were often received through dreams, visions, revelations, and inner prompting.

Most of the world's spiritual traditions attribute many of their teachings to have come from a divine source, and have created rituals and practices to enable one to connect with this reality. Throughout history, mystics, artists, philosophers, warriors and scientists have claimed to receive guidance from the Divine. Moses, Buddha, Socrates, Jesus, Mohammed, Rumi, Michelangelo, Mozart, Harriet Tubman, Wallace Black Elk, Gandhi, Winston Churchill, Carl Jung, General George Patton and Martin Luther King have all claimed to be divinely guided and inspired.

The term "divine guidance" refers to a guiding influence originating from an ultimate source of wisdom. This *ultimate source of wisdom* has been viewed as an infinitely expansive aspect of our nature, where self and divine are one, giving rise to inspiration, creativity and intuition. If we are being guided by the unseen, does this occur only on rare occasion or to the spiritually evolved, or is it continual?

The great Indian sage Ramana Maharshi said, "One comes into existence for a certain purpose. That purpose will be accomplished whether one considers oneself the actor or not." Just as each tree and animal plays a vital role in maintaining nature's balance, I believe human beings also have a particular makeup. After years of working with infants and young children, I realized that each of us comes into this world with a specific nature.

Marcus Aurelius expressed this beautifully when he said "Each thing has come into existence for a specific purpose, like a horse or a grapevine. Even the sun would say: 'I exist for a purpose,' and also the other gods... everyone must do what is in accordance with their constitution..." I have often said that we are each different kinds of trees.

Some trees are tall, thin, and sway easily, while others have thicker trunks and less elasticity. Some trees are very inviting because they bear fruit or flowers, while others have thorns, making it impossible to get close to them. Like trees, we are all different, serving a different purpose in maintaining nature's balance.

Our nature defines the fundamental way we see the world, our disposition or temperament, and the abilities and knowledge we appear to have been born with -- those things we know by heart. To a great degree our nature determines who we are in the world, what we stand for, and who or what we are drawn to. Just as an apple doesn't fall far from the tree, the core purpose of our life is an expression of our basic nature or makeup.

This core purpose emits a unique energetic fingerprint or field that continually interacts with the environment, influencing what enters our awareness and becomes the focus of our attention. After looking back and examining my life, I now realize that all my experiences were stepping stones in achieving my destiny.

Perhaps, the human energy system is a homeopathic remedy, continually attracting the precise experiences necessary to heighten awareness and catalyze evolution. Marcus Aurelius said, "...The entire universe is one great harmony...all things are mutually intertwined..." Maybe our awakening is about embracing the uniqueness and unity of our nature.

A few years ago, my daughter Gina asked me to sit outside

with her, as she wanted to discuss something. As we sat on the lanai, she began to share something that had occurred the day before, and asked if I thought she had made the right decision. As I sat with her question, something pulled my eyes towards a large tree moving back and forth in the neighbor's yard. I had a revelation.

I turned to Gina and said, "Do you see that?"

She said, "What, the tree?"

"Yes. What do you notice?"

"It's swaying," she said.

"Now, if you didn't know that wind existed, you might think that the tree was moving itself. But since you know wind exists, even though you can't see it, you know that it's the wind that's actually innervating the movement of the tree."

"That's right," she said.

I then asked, "What do you think is *moving the wind?*" As she looked at me and paused, I said, "Something even more invisible, eh?"

"I suppose," she replied.

I then looked at her and said, "In the midst of our lives, we see others continually moving about, and at those moments forget about the invisible wind."

After that incident, I began noticing how often in my life I am guided by that invisible force. I started remembering powerful incidences during my childhood and as an adult that led me to realize that this phenomenon had been going on my entire life. The only difference was that now I was more aware of it.

In contrast to my personal experience of feeling guided by life, I often hear the expression, "We create our own reality," where fulfilling our desires is equated with success, while getting what we don't want indicates that we have yet not learned how to properly focus our thoughts. At the heart of this idea is making the right choices, having clear intentions, and learning how to use our thoughts to create what we want — from health and happiness to prosperity and success.

Since this was not my experience, I began investigating the lives of those who had supposedly awoken and attained enlightenment. Did Jesus, Lao Tzu, and Ramana Maharshi speak about getting what they wanted, or were they *choiceless,* living in a state of unconditional acceptance?

In the Gospel of Thomas, Jesus is quoted as saying, "When you make the two one ... the inside like the outside and the outside like the inside ... the above like the below ... the male and the female one and the same ... then will you enter the Kingdom."

Lao Tzu said, "Life is a series of natural and spontaneous changes. Don't resist them — that only creates sorrow. Let reality be reality. Let things flow naturally forward in whatever way they like." Also, "Be content with what you have; rejoice in the way things are. When you realize there is nothing lacking, the whole world belongs to you."

Ramana Maharshi said, "Everything is predestined. Whatever is destined not to happen will not happen, try as you may. Whatever is destined to happen will happen, do what you may to prevent it. This is certain. Leave it to the Higher Power; you cannot renounce or retain as you choose."

Are we continually making choices and moving ourselves from place to place, or is something invisible constantly directing our every move? Is there an intelligence that directs and innervates the movement of all things? If only we could see through the eyes of God.

What if life already offers us evidence that we are being guided, giving us glimpses of infinite vision *when we are not looking for it?* To understand what it truly means to see, we must discover *who or what is actually seeing.* And, if we are fortunate enough to perceive that, we might notice that we are not living life, life is living us.

Throughout our lives, we have been conditioned to believe that thinking was the apex of the evolutionary process, and that humans were the most evolved creatures because we were the only ones who could think. But isn't most thinking simply an attempt to guarantee that things come out our way? Isn't thinking often just a fancy word for worrying?

Do we really learn by what we call thinking, or do the revelations in our life enter our awareness free of charge, while we're not looking for them? Could it be that trying to figure things out actually obscures the realization that life is guiding our every move, and that true genius comes to us, rather than from us? Perhaps we are designed to respond to life, rather than lead it.

In the late 70's, I was asked to give a one-hour presentation to a group of graduate students at a local University. I spent hours preparing my speech and made notes on about 40 index cards. As I walked towards the podium after being introduced, I realized that I had prepared, written down and rehearsed every sentence of a lecture about a subject I was supposedly an expert on.

All of a sudden the 40 index cards I was holding slipped out of my hand, falling all over the floor. It happened so fast that I had no time to pick up the cards — so I just stepped behind the podium and tried to collect myself.

After what seemed like an eternity, I took a deep breath and shared with the audience what had happened and the realization I had. The entire group and I then sighed in unison as if the weight of the world had been lifted from our shoulders.

My one-hour presentation about learning disabilities turned into a three-hour informal discussion about learning without effort. I was not prepared for the miracle that occurred that day! I learned that I never had to prepare anything again, as long as I shared only what I knew by heart. Since that day, whenever I am asked to speak in public, I show up empty-handed and allow life to guide me.

When my children were very young they would often play with certain toys and just leave them out when they were finished playing. I repeatedly asked them to put their toys away after they were finished with them. However, that only seemed to work at the moment I mentioned it. No matter what I said or did, they kept going back to their old habit of not putting their toys away. So, after a while I was inspired to see whether I myself was doing what I was asking them to do. I began wondering what would happen if I automatically responded to everything that entered my awareness. As I began noticing all the things I noticed, I realized there was a significant difference between the thoughts I was having and those that were having me. One originated within my own mind chatter, and the other spontaneously entered my awareness out of nothingness.

Once this difference became more obvious to me, I began an around-the-clock practice. It went like this: anything that entered my awareness became my responsibility, anything that was my responsibility I would be present with, and anything I was present with I would complete. I did this practice for a week and didn't let anything get by me. Towards the end of the week I was picking up cigarette butts off the street. In the process, I became intricately aware of how often I was trying to figure out "what to do with my life," and how, as I became more aware of this habit, it began to change. I finally realized that awareness is curative. As I became aware of things they changed. Not because I tried to change them, but because I was now aware of them. When I was busy trying to see what to do next, there was no clarity in sight. However, when this unconscious habit became more obvious, I began noticing that clarity entered my awareness, automatically, moving my eyes to the next step in my life's journey.

It has been more than 30 years since I first began that practice. Now it defines who I am. Responding to whatever enters my awareness is the foundation of my life. As we become aware of everything that touches us, we begin noticing what is truly essential. Although we are not looking with our eyes, our eyesight often improves, and our insight becomes so acute that we realize that we have never really seen with our eyes. And yet, "The eyes are the windows of the soul." So how are the eyes related to seeing at a deep level?

In my youth, I had excellent eyesight but still had difficulty paying attention and reading comfortably. Whenever I started reading I would fall asleep within a couple of minutes. However, the doctor said I had 20/20 vision and told my parents that there was nothing wrong with my eyes. I tried very hard in school but still found it challenging and, consequently, thought there was something wrong with me.

When I started college, the reading demand was so hard on my eyes that I became nearsighted and was given glasses. I will never forget that experience. I was in the middle of a test, looked up at the blackboard, and all of a sudden noticed that it was all blurry. Although it cleared up within a few minutes, I immediately went to the infirmary to see what was wrong. The doctor told me that I was just nearsighted and gave me a pair of glasses. Although I could see better, the more I wore the glasses, the worse my vision became and reading was still very challenging. It seemed like every six months I got stronger glasses, but still couldn't read for more than a few minutes without falling asleep.

When I entered optometry school the reading demand increased even more, and my eyes continued to worsen. At the end of my second year, I was struggling to keep a 2.0 grade point average and thought for sure I would be asked to leave.

In my third year, I was instructed to go to the clinic and have a vision exam. The student who examined me said my eyes had gotten worse and that I needed a stronger prescription. He also pointed out that my eyes were not working well together and recommended I do vision exercises with a device he loaned me. Unfortunately, I never used it.

One day I was sitting in bed reading one of my assignments and, as usual, fell asleep. When I opened my eyes, the first thing I noticed was the vision training device I had been given. Without a thought I picked it up, did the exercises for just five minutes, then proceeded to read for an hour at a level of comfort and comprehension I had never experienced before.

I don't know what caused me to pick up and use the device at that moment. However, I was so moved by what had taken place that I started to cry. I did the exercises daily for two months, and then made the Dean's List nearly every quarter until I graduated.

That experience led to a great interest in how the eyes, brain, mind and awareness were involved in the process of seeing. I learned that the eyes are not separate from the brain, but actual frontal extensions of the brain — two satellite dishes that connect the outer world with our inner world. I also discovered that 85 - 90 % of the information we take in during our lifetime enters by way of the eyes. Vision is our navigational system, and is inseparably connected to everything we do. In sighted individuals, vision determines how we "see" life, and is the key to understanding our behavior, emotional make-up and intelligence.

I once heard someone say that God's most precious gift is sight. But what does that mean? Most people think vision is just eyesight. But vision is not just what we see; *it's what we do with what we see*. It is our response to life, inseparable from consciousness, and at the heart of understanding who and what we are. *But what is seeing through the eyes, and is it perceiving or projecting the world we experience, or a combination of both?*

When I began practicing optometry in 1973, I noticed that most of my patients were having the same experience I had. Many of them had difficulties in school and most of them ended up wearing glasses because their eyes were getting weaker from year to year. Based on the profound changes I had with my own vision while in optometry school, I realized that being a vision specialist was going to involve a lot more than just examining eyes and prescribing glasses.

Generally, you know someone is paying attention because they're looking at you. To look at you, their eyes must *aim*. So the ability of the eyes to efficiently aim lays the foundation for one's capacity to be present and attentive.

As the eyes aim they also *focus*, allowing life to become clear and understandable. That's why "I see" means *I understand*, and why all meditative practices have you focus on something. Interestingly, whether our eyes are open or closed, when we focus on something, our eyes respond in exactly the same way.

So, as the eyes aim and focus, the foundation is laid for our ability to experience presence and attentiveness with each other and the world around us. If our eyes are not able to accomplish that easily, we will experience difficulty learning, both in the classroom and in the world.

Our eyes are designed to work together; each providing a slightly different perspective, which when fused creates the miracle of stereoscopic (3-D) vision. Stereoscopic vision, described by Gesell as "the crown jewel of organic evolution," literally and figuratively provides us greater depth. It also acts as the body's *prioritization system*, allowing us to immediately know what is calling us from the outside world, and most importantly what is guiding the next step of our journey.

CHAPTER 11

Dr. Rapaille

Business of Disease

Diseases are a part of life. We get sick, look for a cure, and hopefully regain health - until the next time.

Humans are programmed to survive as long as possible.

In order to do that, we buy food, vitamins, go to the doctor and take medications.

Disease, of course, is a big business; like food, sex and violence (guns).

Can we really influence people to buy products that they do not really need or want?

People believe that good marketing can sell anything, but I do not think that this is good marketing and advertising.

Think about the Soviet Union. They had a captive audience, total control of the media, an army to dispose of opponents (gulag) and all the subliminal marketing and psychological tools to manipulate people's minds.

After three generations of trying to reprogram people, the Berlin Wall fell, and religion (referred to as the "Opium of the people") reappeared everywhere.

If all of their marketing, advertising, propaganda and mind manipulations were so effective, why didn't they succeed?

Because good marketing is to discover the unspoken, unaware, unaddressed and unconscious needs of the people. These are the real needs!

The business of disease should be about the same - understanding the real needs of people. Americans are adolescents, and this is an adolescent culture. Adolescence means the permanent search for an identity. "I do not know what I am going to do when I grow up, and I never want to grow up" (forever young). To help people stay younger and look younger is not just good business, it is the fulfillment of a cultural need.

We can say that the business of disease is completely influenced by cultures, but to address the real unconscious and unaddressed needs of people and culture, one must discover the culture code. Americans will do anything to stay young.

Science is in the business of anxiety in the U.S. It creates more anxiety in the business of disease, and does not bring peace and closure. For example, one day coffee is bad for your health, and the next day scientific research tells you that coffee is good for your health. New research always means less certainty and more anxiety. So we try to cure anxiety. But to cure is not to treat the symptoms; it is to find the cause and the real problem, i.e. "I have a headache because I do not want to go to school."

Good business is curing the disease: "Why don't I want to go to school?", and bad business is only treating the symptoms by curing the headache.

The more diet books we sell, the more people are overweight. Why? Because diet books are just treating the symptoms.

People know that they should eat less and exercise more, and yet they do not. Despite all the campaigns, new products and diets, we are a nation of obese.

Lawyers are in the business of disease. Dow Company went bankrupt even though there was no scientific evidence to prove that their product created disease. Lawyers, on the other hand, are in the business of creating more business through imaginary diseases.

Treating disease and curing disease clearly should not be a business, just as food from a garden or sex. Today, disease, like food and sex has become big business.

The reptilian brain cannot be fooled too often and for too long. We should go back to the Mother archetype. Your mother took care of you when you were sick and fed you all the time. That was not business. It was love.

To bring clean water to Africa, contraception to India, and clean air to China is a duty, a must. I do believe that solving problems, caring for people, for their property and dreams deserves retribution. The problem starts when the higher purpose disappears and only making money becomes the goal.

Chinese baby milk has killed children just as fake medications have made people sicker.

Everyone should be against these practices. Decoding the unconscious structure that keeps people buying the wrong things, doing the wrong things and getting worse is the only way to modify their behavior, and to help them fight and prevent disease. We should concentrate on rewarding those who help others and who do what is good for the people.

The Pasteur Institute is not in the business of disease but in making breakthrough discoveries; preventing and curing diseases.

Corporations need profit in order to invest in research and good businesses want their clients to grow, be healthy and move up. They do this by discovering and adding products and medications that are needed. We also need to understand how every culture has a different perspective on health, beauty, medicine, disease and cures.

Medicine and Culture, by Lynn Payer, is a good example of how the same problem – breast cancer – is approached and treated so differently in various cultures.

We can also consider why hip replacement is so much more costly in the United States than in Belgium. This is not just a business problem. This is a bureaucratic problem. Bureaucrats who are in the business of increasing their power are transforming the Medical culture and Medical practices. Their number one mission is to delay any crucial decisions, create more regulations and hire more bureaucrats. In this case, the business of disease becomes deadly.

In ancient China, the principle was to pay your doctor when you were healthy, and to stop paying him when you were sick. Doctors at that time were highly motivated to keep you healthy. These physicians were not in the business of disease, but in the business of keeping people healthy.

This should be the direction for all healthcare providers, doctors, nurses, hospitals and pharmaceutical companies. It should be their priority.

Conclusion: Decoding the real reptilian needs associated with health, wellness and beauty should be our higher purpose. Feeling good, happy, moving, moving up, growing, improving and enjoying life should also be our higher purpose. Treating people as an element of a system involves treating the entire family and being on code with the culture.

Treating the symptoms should only be a temporary solution and we should never forget to cure the syndrome by discovering its cause (etiology.)

CHAPTER 12

Patricia Bisch

Can You Change Your Body Weight With Your Mind?

Food is the glue that holds my fragmented parts together, so I look whole and no one can see I am really in pieces. The outside world is beating me up emotionally. I don't feel that I have a buffer strong enough to shield me from the onslaught of predatory comments and critical judgments. Food is my protector. Like a loving parent, it shelters me from feeling unloved, anxious and out of control. There is so much fear inside of me. I am eating to numb my pain and give myself the love I am so desperately needing. I feel so alone. – Patricia Bisch

To an idealizing child of 10, my father was no less than perfect. I was the star who could do no wrong, and he was the wind beneath my sails. But when my sister was born (who later became the homecoming queen), he turned his attention to her. Like all children, I searched for the flaw in me that had made him shift his affection and decided I must not be pretty enough. I prayed his attention would return. It never did.

When we moved to Beverly Hills, fighting and anger filled my house; and when I was 16, my parents divorced. My father lied to me about a betrayal and, with overwhelming sadness, my heart closed. I turned to food, bingeing and dieting to kill the pain and it didn't help that my skin began breaking out at the same time. Having been disconnected from my own beauty and lovability, I was hiding my aloneness with food.

By my early 20s, I wondered if I would ever be *happy again,* but one day a close friend lovingly invited me to a Mind/Body class that he thought might lift my spirits. In the class I studied how to heal any disease or bodily condition by altering *specific thoughts and emotions. However, this teaching was not about weight.* After 8 years of weekly studies and still feeling deeply sad, *I finally decided that it was time* to put this Mind/Body knowledge to the test with my personal issue around food.

I told the teacher that I was a compulsive eater, much like any addict, and explained that I had absolutely no control over my eating. *I was a junk food junkie.* There are overweight people who eat only healthy food or eat very little – and still gain weight. That was *not* me.

The teacher agreed that it was time to prove to myself the power of my thinking, and asked me to write down different thoughts and personal experiences, which I refer to in my book *Freedom From Food,* as my meditation. "I want you to read this meditation 10 minutes a day, every day for two weeks," he said in a confident manner. "But before you start, get on the scale and note what you weigh. Then, for the next two weeks, *eat whatever you want, whenever you want it.* At the end of this period, you will get back on the scale and see that you have not gained weight."

This was a scary proposition. Although I was only about 30 pounds overweight, I was at my highest weight, at the peak of my bingeing activity and compulsively eating out of control. There was no way I could risk gaining even another 5-10 pounds. I felt desperate and I knew nothing else had worked. So even though the process would mean that I would be eating my usual *favorite liquor store junk food like chips, candy bars, ice cream and little cakes in endless quantities,* I decided to do it anyway.

So for two weeks I did eat as expected, and then, with a little fear but with trust in the process I stepped on the scale. When I looked down I could not believe what I saw. *I had not gained any weight!*

This completely blew my mind!! Yes, of course I understood theoretically what had happened, but this was physical proof! The numbers couldn't lie. Until this moment, my understanding of the Mind/Body connection had been intellectual. Now it was real.

Looking down at the scale and thinking about my bingeing over the last two weeks, I knew that it "should" have shown I'd gained *10 -15 pounds* – but it was saying *I had not gained any weight* at all!

I needed a moment to think this through. *If my mind could keep me from gaining weight, why couldn't I direct my intention and focus to losing weight?* Over the next six weeks I did just that, focusing on being my ideal weight and making no attempt at all to control my eating. And it worked! At the end of six weeks, I was at my perfect weight! *I knew* that *something profound and life-changing had just happened and that I would never be the same.*

I had just experienced a miracle, an epiphany that proved to me I could change my body system with intention and extreme focus, rather than with exercise and dieting. I assumed that I also had shifted my metabolism, since I was no longer gaining weight no matter what I ate. To me this was on the same level as healers who transform cancer cells into normal cells. But this wasn't being done by a yogi, this was me – just a regular person.

It has been 30 years since that life-changing moment on the scale, and *I have never gained back the weight.* I had actually *transmuted my food with my thoughts,* and I was compelled to create the *Freedom From Food* program that empowers others who are suffering to do the same.

I am now what I call an *Advanced Eater* who can make food choices for mental clarity, mental focus, and to have more energy. Choices that just make me feel better like eating fruit instead of ice cream, if I need to eat something before bed. At times I choose Rice Dream instead of ice cream. This ability to *choose* only happened after I no longer felt deprived. I knew without a doubt that it was my mind that created my weight. Quite honestly, I was eating junk food when I lost all my weight, although I did not feel as good or alive. It gave me the opportunity to see quite clearly that my weight loss was purely caused by changing my thoughts. We are *so much more powerful then we imagine!*

Food and Our Body Are Energy

Can anyone do what I did? From my own personal healing and from experience in working with individuals and groups for 30 years, my answer is *"YES!"* Does everyone have this power to influence their body weight? Yes!

Recent advances in quantum physics reveal that the material world is an optical illusion. We are not solely what we see. When my healing happened, this idea was not being discussed, but now quantum physicists have substantiated the mind/body connection. There is abundant scientific evidence that our thoughts and emotions directly affect our physical form. And although the world appears to be stationary to the naked eye, and our bodies, our weight, and the food we eat appear to be solid, we are composed of constantly moving and *fluctuating energy* which is mostly empty space.

In the material, Newtonian world, where most people's consciousness resides, food and weight become sluggish and stuck. People feel victimized and entrapped by the food they eat. They are unaware of the power of their words. They don't understand that the real trap is in what they are thinking. Their thoughts are what command the fluctuating energy that must comply. When people say, "This ice cream will go right to my hips," they are sculpting the energy right in. Then they blame the ice cream! We believe we can joke with our friends and call ourselves 'ugly' and 'fat', and say mean things about ourselves without consequences. However, the subtleties of our words are registering on us and in us all the time.

Remember, energy from our beliefs flows where our attention goes. It is my observation that this is why some people gain weight no matter what they eat, and some people remain thin although they eat a lot. The energy is following the beliefs they hold. For people who are out-of-control eaters like me, it was a great source of relief to find that I actually could control and *choose* the words to create the body I wanted to live in, and that doing this was actually more important than the food I ate.

I invite you to try this new way of thinking right now. Don't put your attention on the body you don't want, or focus on the parts of your body you are feeling ashamed of. Take a moment and put your attention on the body you *do* want and just visualize it for a minute. Think of it as energy - mostly empty space. See it as champagne bubbles of energy that move around and rearrange with your thoughts. Hold the thought that everything you eat makes you lighter and lighter. No rush. Breathe it in... feel it... let the feeling expand... and then expand again, feeling a lightness.

Now to help you further grasp the concept of food as energy, think of it as if it were air. Air is light and permeable and has no apparent substance. You ingest it continuously in great quantities, and it just passes in and out of you unobstructed. *Food is a mindless, non-intentional, neutral energy.* You would never think air could cause you to gain weight. You simply take it in and release it while breathing, without attaching any other thoughts to it.

Think of food the same way; as a mindless, non-intentional, fluctuating neutral energy. Are you beginning to feel differently about food and weight?

Scientific Evidence

After my weight loss experience, I never saw physical reality in the same way again. I was now keenly aware of the non-material world and thought of *everything as energy.* From this perspective, you can examine your essence, the pure consciousness that exists before form, as well as your ability to create from this non-actualized place. Think about it: your body, cells and the food you eat are composed of this unified, living energy field that is continuously changing. It is from here that our ideas create and coagulate into what appears as matter.

Whether it's chocolate cake, an apple, a chair or a rock, it is all energy directed by your mind. Energy cannot think or have bad intentions. A chocolate cake cannot decide to make one person gain weight and another person be thin. In and of itself, a cake cannot make you do or be anything. It certainly has no brain. As funny as it sounds, try sitting in front of some candy and just looking at it. See if it can make you stand up or raise your hand. I doubt it, because it's energy without the power to think at all.

Scientists, doctors and researchers are proving to us the importance now of knowing that if we are worried about our bodies (in our case our weight), then we better pay close attention to the thoughts we are activating. "Body and mind are one. The body is the actual outward manifestation, in physical space, of the mind," *says* Candace B. Pert, PhD, in her book *Molecules of Emotion.* "Mind is the matrix of all matter," *says* Max Planck, physicist and Nobel Prize winner.

Masura Emoto, a doctor of alternative medicine, has done extensive research on a related subject: the connection between consciousness and water. Since our bodies are 70 percent water, his research is essential to understanding how our mental activity affects our weight. Emoto studied how water responds to words. His findings show that water crystals became distorted and imploded when confronted with negative words such as "You make me sick." However, words such as *love* and *gratitude* produced beautiful water crystal patterns.

Right now, let yourself pause and say some kind words to your body. Feel the way it responds. Try saying, "Everything I eat makes me lighter and lighter, and I trust my body to take what it needs from the food I eat and release the rest," and see how it feels. Remember, *whenever you direct your focus, energy starts moving* toward that reality. It might take a little time to manifest a thought, so try saying it again: "Everything I eat makes me lighter and lighter, and I trust my body to take what it needs from the food I eat and release the rest." This time close your eyes and stay with that thought. See how it expands and ripples throughout your body, and notice any changes that occur. We are moving so fast in our world these days that we do not linger long enough on good thoughts to allow them to expand. How often does your mind habitually drift toward judgments and negative thoughts? Your job is to slow it down and expand the thoughts you would like to manifest.

Here are some more examples of how our thinking is affecting our body. In 2011 the Noetic Digest published a story about Russian scientists who have discovered that it is possible for our DNA to be reprogrammed by words and frequencies. Other scientists have documented that the presence of an observer affects the motion of tiny nanoparticles of matter. If the observer expects these particles to behave in a certain way, they will. Studies have shown that at the moment of observation by a conscious mind, an electron "chooses" what it will do based on the observer's expectations.

Scientist David Albert, author of *Quantum Mechanics and Experience,* concurs that our conscious minds direct the actions of these particles, changing the universe from a vague collection of possibilities into the more definite reality that we know. This evidence supports the belief held by many that our conscious choices allow the universe to select what it will be, how it will appear, and how it will behave.

In his book, *The Isaiah Effect*, scientist Gregg Braden remarks that the choices we make take place in a field of energy that exists in every aspect of creation. This field has intelligence that responds to emotions and thoughts. These scientists are just a few who are letting us know that it is important to make it a loving practice to choose more carefully the thoughts we are thinking.

In the *Freedom From Food* program, we examine how these scientific conclusions are affecting our weight. We deduce that, at the subatomic level, our bodies are also directly influenced by our thinking and emotions, and will always follow our expectations.

In the case of food, for example, you might believe that bread and butter make you gain weight. Take a moment to imagine what happens as a result of this belief. It logically follows that your body will be reorganizing around this expectation. Rather than releasing unneeded energy automatically, your body will begin to hold onto it.

Your consciousness is most likely bombarded with countless thoughts about food, both self-imposed and from the outside world, and your mind is constantly accepting and rejecting one concept after another. "Don't eat this. It has too many calories." "Don't eat that. It has too many carbohydrates or too much fat." These messages create mistrust. "Your body can't handle this food," they say. "You are going to get fat." Words and fears from the outside seep into your mind and bombard your perfectly ordered inner ecosystem. Eventually, instead of a clear, flowing stream, your thoughts become a dam of confusion, causing your body to hold onto food that it would otherwise metabolize efficiently and then effortlessly eliminate.

Are you thinking like Teflon or Velcro? Are you letting excess food energy slide off your nonstick surface, or are you holding onto it like you'll never let go?

Childhood Obesity and Emotional Pain

I grew up in Beverly Hills, the home of the superficial. My mother used to say, "Isn't that person the most fantastic person?" When I asked what she liked about them, she'd say," Did you see that face?" I grew to understand that in her mind, these people were fabulous and great because they were good-looking. In

Beverly Hills that meant they had star quality – they were perfect by Hollywood's norm. Perfect hair, body, skin. Of course most people feel ugly and shamed and "not enough" when held up to those lofty standards. In fact, 80% of all women think they are overweight, and it's easy to see why.

Our children are bombarded by the media with anorexic, bulimic models and movie stars who seem to grab all the attention. As a result, children are starting to diet at a very young age, thinking they *must* do it to get the love they so desperately need. Kids who are overweight suffer terrible bullying, and teens are getting Botox injections and breast implants. They are treating themselves like empty shells, forgetting that the values they hold on the inside matter. People are beating themselves up emotionally and depriving themselves so that they will not have an ounce of fat on their bones, which they are convinced, would make them unlovable.

Having food problems or issues begins in a deep, painful, emotional place inside of us when we are not given the love we need, or we are betrayed, abandoned or abused. As a result, we feel deeply disconnected from ourselves, others, and Spirit; we decide that in some way we are defective. On the inside, we feel alone and out of control. At these times, whether we are children, teens or adults, we begin to think that if we were only thin enough or pretty enough, we would be loved. As overeaters, or as the parents of children who are overeaters, we begin to reach for an *outside fix* like diets, pills, shots or exercise programs to help our children.

I feel that there is an important piece missing in these approaches. That missing piece has to do with helping children and teens who are obese to develop an *inner empowerment,* which includes a love of their own body type, and a reconnection with their body's natural healing abilities to assist with their weight problem.

It's important to explain that some people are naturally very thin and beautiful while others have a different, beautiful, voluptuous, rounder body. We are all different. I recommend taking your children out into nature and showing them how trees, animals, insects, and flowers don't diet yet are perfect just the way they are. They are not too fat and not too thin. They have a 'just right' look. You would never call a tree, flower or insect fat. Remind your children that they are part of nature, too; and this natural proportion lives inside of them, even if they can't see it. Awaken their knowing that their body is trying to heal itself all the time and return to this perfect proportion. Reconnect them with the understanding that their body is on their side.

Remind your children and yourself of the body's amazing ability to heal *automatically*. When I was a small child, I fell down and scraped my knee. Seeing blood on my knee was scary. I wasn't sure what it meant or what would happen to me. However, soon I learned that no matter how often I fell down and scraped my knee, my body would somehow take care of itself. It would *dependably* send out white blood cells to kill the bacteria. Then my blood would clot and my skin would form a scab. In time, the scab would go away. No matter how many times I fell down, my body always healed itself like clockwork in an elegant dance of health.

This is the miracle – the wondrous way the body mends, even when we don't do a thing! I did not have to say affirmations ("My knee is now healing, my knee is now healing"). I wasn't even old enough to understand what an affirmation was. I discovered that *I could count on my body*—whether I was awake or asleep—to heal all wounds. Hippocrates said, "The natural healing force within us is the greatest force in getting well."

People who are thin (meaning in their perfect proportion) rely on this pull in the body to always maintain ideal weight. They never question it. They have a knowing that unneeded food will move right through them and not add extra pounds--and it does.

Allow yourself to imagine this happening in your own body. Take a moment and mentally zoom inside. Visualize yourself eating a cookie or an avocado. Then picture an inner team that immediately takes the cookie or the avocado and begins to break it down. The team takes from the food what your body needs and eliminates the rest. See your body as a unified organism, efficient and precise, moving the food directly into the digestive system and then to various organs. Without interference, watch how your food is transformed smoothly until all excess is eliminated. In the next few months, if your children can begin to understand these principles, they can count on this force and *be able to relax more when they are eating*.

In my healing, and in the people I work with, the answer to losing weight was not on the outside. The answer was in recognizing that I had the power that was needed right inside of me all the time. I could deal with my emotions and heal my heart and *choose* the thoughts about food that I wanted to manifest. I was not a victim. I could also create a loving, nurturing adult to have an inner dialogue with me every day to heal my wounded soul.

If children or adults ask me, "What do you do if you feel too full because you ate too much? Don't you worry about gaining weight and getting fat? Don't you worry that you may get heavier?" My answer is "No!" I *trust* my body. If I am full, the feeling may go away in an hour, or it may take overnight. However, my body *always* handles it, and I know that food is energy and mostly empty space. I trust my body to do its *natural job of elimination, and bring me back to a state of equilibrium and balance*. I understand that food is just energy and has no power over me. I have been permanently healed for thirty years and live a vibrant, healthy life as a thin person. I know that it is not what I eat that makes me fat.

Conclusion

As I began this chapter, I spoke about the terrible pain I had when I lost my father's love and felt betrayed. Thirty years later, I now understand that getting my father to love me, attracting love from a man, and my father's rejection, maybe really had nothing to do with my looks. As hard as I tried to be pretty, that still didn't get me what I wanted. It was only when I valued myself in the highest way that I could lose weight and receive love. It came as a reflection of the *deep inner work* I did on myself, and my understanding of *how powerful my mind was*.

I love myself now. There is a warm, compassionate feeling in my heart. I can see my incredible strengths and my weaknesses. Yes, there have been passages through dark nights of the soul, revisiting some horrible places; yet what remains is my deep gratitude and amazement for the miracle that has happened. The benefits of learning to deeply connect with my Inner Child and the amazing knowing that I discovered about how to focus my mind and emotions has healed and empowered me. What a miracle to realize that I did have the power all along, right inside of me, and how wonderful to tell you that this power also exists within you.

CHAPTER 13

Rita Soman, MA, CADC III

Is Addiction Really An Incurable Disease?

We have been programmed to believe that addiction to alcohol and drugs is genetically transmitted and an incurable disease. Typically, once such a diagnosis has been made, behavior modification therapy and participation in 12-step programs such as AA (Alcoholic Anonymous) or NA (Narcotics Anonymous) is prescribed, as well as medications for those individuals who can't curb the urge to drink/use. Unfortunately using current methodology have not ensured successful treatment outcome for many who continue to fall victims in the vicious cycle of relapse.

For 18 years I worked as a psychotherapist with addicted clients, I often wondered, why the addicted individuals struggled with their addictions, in spite of doing everything they were taught. The following discovery completely altered my perception and introduced me to the methods I have been using in my private practice, successfully.

The Problem

Addictions are really a result of an embedded problem with self-esteem or shame or guilt. It's an embedded message. When you use this process you get to the root of it, and you are not replacing one symptom with the another and that happens a lot in traditional therapy, people will Stop drinking; start smoking. Stop smoking; start drinking too much coffee.

"We sabotage ourselves due to deeply embedded, shame, guilt and self-loathing," says Dr. Walter Jacobson, psychiatrist and author of, Forgive to Win.

We have been using mainly psychotherapy, which rely almost exclusively on "insight" and "motivation," seldom create real and lasting changes because these methods do not address the cause of addictions, that lies in the subconscious mind. The fact is that very few people really have the capacity to benefit from insight based psychotherapy. It takes much work and a lot of time to do insight oriented psychotherapy and really get people to look at their root issues and gain the kind of light bulb going off ah-ha kind of insight phenomenon. Intellectually they may understand their problems but they don't have the kind of insight where real healing happens at that core level.

The Discovery

In the book, The Biology of Belief, Dr. Bruce Lipton shares the latest scientific discoveries about the biochemical nature of brain function and that, specifically, every cell in our body is affected by our thoughts, both positive and negative. Yes! Our CELLS are affected by our THOUGHTS!!!! Signals from the outside or said another way, the environment, control our genes, DNA, and cells - including energetic messages stemming from our thoughts, whether positive or negative. In the simplest terms, this means that we need to change the way we think if we are to heal addictions. Dr. Lipton said, "The function of the mind is to create coherence between our beliefs and the reality we experience, what that means is that your mind will adjust the body's biology and behavior to fit with your beliefs."

If you've been told addiction is incurable and you are powerless and your mind believes it, you most likely will continue to stop drinking or drug taking behavior. There's the part of you that swears it doesn't want to drink/use (the conscious mind), trumped by the part that believes you will (the addiction prognosis mediated by the subconscious mind), which then throws into gear the chemical reaction (mediated by the brain's chemistry) to make sure the body conforms to the dominant belief.

Dr. Lipton said that it comes down to how the subconscious mind, which contains our deepest beliefs, has been programmed. It is these beliefs that ultimately cast the deciding vote. Since the subconscious programs operate outside the range of consciousness, we don't experience ourselves playing out these behaviors. Therefore, we don't even see ourselves sabotaging our own lives, and as a result, we don't take responsibility for the lives we lead. We see ourselves as victims of forces outside of our control. It's hard to own what we've done our whole lives. So we perceive ourselves as victims, and we believe that genes are in control.

The Solution

So what is the solution? The solution lies in your ability to create alignment between the conscious and subconscious minds. Not many people know that the subconscious mind can be re-programmed easily.

The Method

Developed by a psychotherapist, Robert M. Williams, PSYCH-K® process effectively identifies the root cause of addictions; then interrupting and altering the life-long patterns of behaviors to render positive, long termed results. It uses the mind/body interface of muscle testing (kinesiology), to access the self-limiting files of the subconscious mind. PSYCH-K process helps people tap into their negative self-definitions and replace them with positive definitions. We do that with a series of new suggestions, new definitions. It's almost like post hypnotic suggestions where these new definitions replace the old ones. This process is a way to cut through all the stuff that therapy and medication can't get to. It's a way of synchronizing the communication between the left and right hemisphere.

The Results

You go back to the core level and build their self-esteem, build their self-confidence, and eliminate the unresolved issues from the past. Once the old programming is replaced by the new, their conscious mind is linked up with their subconscious mind which is no longer sabotaging them. Now it's totally on board with the plan to succeed and be happy.

CHAPTER 14

Sonia Barrett

Your life is Your Own

Life is an incredible journey. It is both a joyous and maddening experience all at the same time. Life is an experience we crave and even in our dark moments we cling to life. My observation since childhood brought about an awareness of how few questions are asked by most about the mechanism of the body; these uniquely designed vessels that seem to keep going under the most extreme conditions. What I came to realize is the degree to which the average person relies on someone else to keep them informed of their body's health. A tremendous amount of trust is placed in the hands of others in managing these incredible vehicles we call a body.

I became observant of the tremendous flood of outside influences in shaping our lives. Health care in the Western World seem to consist largely of pharmaceutically supported medicine, mutilations and a series of quick fixes to erase symptoms but never a cure. This has been an accepted system for quite some time. Fear is a tool used to encourage participation; vaccines, flu shots, shingles virus, whooping cough, fibromyalgia, cancer and the list goes on.

Perhaps when we begin to better understand the relationship between our emotions and our body, the notion that "an ounce of prevention is better than an ounce of cure" will be the focal point in what we will strive for. We have all experienced the body's response to fear, shock, shame, sadness, hurt, joy, happiness, laughter, and an assortment of emotions. There is evidence of this when the body responds through a stomach ache or a headache or shivers, the heart beats fast, and blood pressure rises and so on. Yet despite such obvious signs, emotions are not brought into the equation when extreme health conditions such as cancer, diabetes, fibromyalgia or lupus are present.

We are born into a stressful world and for some they are born directly into stressful environments, stressful conditions and family lifestyle. Most often we carry those stresses with us throughout our life without being aware of them. These stored stresses are further compounded by an accumulation of additional stresses as we journey through life.

My inspiration for producing the film *The Business of Disease* was based on my observation and realization of our collective health programs. My observation was of marketing and the subtle but effective ways in which we respond to products, ideas, and concepts presented to us.

For some this material might be new yet, you were drawn to examine the information. Gradually working through this information and slowly digesting it will be the most beneficial way to fuel change. Surely there is a small voice inside you that realizes that there are limitations to your freedom; very basic freedoms that should never be questioned. Your first though is perhaps how to proceed from here and what steps you should take to be more in control of your spirit, mind, and body. Perhaps the first questions should involve determining those areas of your life that feel inhibited or programmed.

If your issues are health related an examination of your methods of self-care is a great start. What is the condition of your emotional health? This doesn't necessarily mean an evaluation of your sanity. Are you happy with your life, are you happy with your relationships, are you holding on to issues from your past, your childhood? What are the conditions of your inner pain?

When did your health issues begin, what were the circumstances in your life at that time? It is not unusual for us to experience dis-ease or ill health after a challenging relationship has ended or the ending of a relationship through the loss of a loved one. Grieving is an essential healing tool and should be welcomed if one has not yet grieved. This will allow the body to release much of the trauma and pain that it might still be holding on to.

Keep in mind that as human beings we are masters at convincing ourselves that we are fine, and so we hide emotional debris away from our self and instead build fences around our hearts and our minds. Although we may have hidden such emotions away, the subconscious mind has recorded it all and so we begin to live from that place. We begin to make choices based on our past but mainly we find ways to protect ourselves. We do what we do best as human beings, "survive".

Every moment is a valid time for change. It is never too late to change the emotional space from which one has been living. We should not be restricted by our age as that too is simply a chronologic program which we have been taught to live by. As long as we are alive there are no cut off dates for choosing to make changes in our lives. Throw out all of the programs and scheduled rules and protocols for living life and simply live. Quantum mechanics has proven that all we have are possibilities. Which possibility we experience is completely up to us. Our perceptual lens and what we believe will be the determining factor in the distance that we will allow our self to go on this journey.

Seek out your passion and let go of conditions that no longer serve you. Just let go! Your life is your own and no one else's. Take responsibility for it and awaken to the possibilities that are there waiting for you to choose freely. Remember that disease is about dis-ease; what is your dis-ease? Own your life without blame of yourself or others. The past happened but this moment is new and every moment is filled with opportunities. We must open our eyes to those opportunities and grab ahold of them. At first you may be met with challenges but you have made it this far and to do so requires strength and fortitude. Most importantly be honest with yourself for that is the key to unlocking your life! Move the old out of the way and make room for the new. Meet the journey from this moment on with optimism and may the road rise up to meet you.

CHAPTER 15

Steven Halpern PhD

Healing Music and Expanded Dimensions of Sound Medicine

For thousands of years, long before 'recorded' history, virtually every culture has known of and revered the healing powers of sound and music. From ancient mythology up through the Bible, this art form was considered a 'gift of the gods'. Sound and music were integral in the healing temples of Egypt and Greece.

Most spiritual and mystical traditions use sound to heal the physical body, and raise the frequency of our vibratory rate to bring us into greater alignment and attunement with the Divine.

Indeed, if a drug were discovered today that could reduce stress, enhance our immune system, change our mood, and do so without harmful side effects; it would either be heralded as a miracle drug or outlawed. So why has there been so little research into the healing powers of sound? And how does it do what it does?

Taking a Look at the Record

Over the past 2,000 years, the role of music devolved from its primary role in the healing arts, and became limited to the realm of entertainment. Over the last 40 years, however, there's been a profound revival of interest in the therapeutic potential of sound and music. The manifestations include music composed without the constraints of traditional classical rules of composition, use of new instruments, and "non-musical" instruments like tuning forks, metal singing bowls, quartz crystal bowls, and toning, harnessing the nonverbal healing potential of the voice.

Indeed, an entire new genre of music developed outside of the traditional music industry; a genre based on the core intention of supporting the health and healing of its audience. Although ignored for many years by mainstream media, record labels and academia, the field has continued to grow exponentially.

Not surprisingly, as the field has grown in popularity and visibility, there's been a flood of misinformation, disinformation and hype that has undermined the integrity and viability of the field. So how can you make sense of all the conflicting claims, opinions masquerading as facts, and disingenuous advertising?

Let me suggest a few guidelines that can help you find the music and sounds that work best for you. One size or sound rarely works for everyone. We have individual responses based on our personal history and taste. But we also share universal characteristics that hold true for everyone. We'll look at these key factors in a moment.

We'll begin by noting that not all 'healing' music is created equal. There is a wide range of quality and expertise available on the market. Some sound healers have over 35 years of experience; others started last year. There are no organizations as yet monitoring 'truth in advertising' with respect to making claims other than 'curing' a specific disease; as there are in the herbal supplement marketplace.

It's up to each individual to develop their own sensitivity, to tune in to the subtle feedback your body, mind and spirit give you. When I began my research in 1970, I was astounded by how few people could accurately identify when they were in a true 'relaxation' state. The situation is better today, but most people still misidentify 'liking' a piece of music versus being relaxed by that selection.

Healing is about 'becoming whole'. For the scope of this discussion, I will focus on music and sound without lyrics, since that involves many other variables. My orientation has centered on supporting our innate healing energies. Researchers like Dr. Herbert Benson discovered how important evoking the 'relaxation response' is to our health and well-being. Although there are many ways to support healing, I've found that the most effective modalities for the largest population base involve shifting the body and mind from ordinary states to a state of deep relaxation.

In a relaxed state, a whole cascade of physical, biochemical and subtle energy responses occur; responses that are still only at the early stages of being understood. Like the allegory of the five blind men and the elephant, many researchers, including neuroscientists, make the mistake that their discipline provides the total understanding of what is going on when, in reality, they are missing a great deal of the subtle energies and 'dark matter' of sound and spirituality.

Five Keys to Sound Healing

When I began my lifelong studies into the mysteries of sound and music, I read that 'music' was 'organized' sound, and involved melody, harmony, rhythm and timbre (tone color). I will suggest that even more fundamental are the factors of vibrational resonance, rhythm entrainment, brainwave entrainment, pattern recognition and the "intention" of the composer/performer.

In the limited space of this chapter, let me give you just two examples that should afford you the same sort of 'aha' moment it has for those who've heard my presentations in lecture or workshop over the past 40 years.

When you're looking to shift gears into relaxation, it's helpful to consider that the generally accepted characteristics of this state involve slowing the heartbeat to below 60 beats per minute and quieting the mind. Most music, however, is composed at a speed (tempo) between 80-120 beats per minute.

Here's the key: As a function of the physical phenomenon of rhythm entrainment, your heartbeat will automatically synchronize (entrain) to the beat of an external rhythmic stimulus, like the beat of the music. Your heart doesn't have a choice. You can't 'tell' it to not match the music. It's an autonomic response.

Prove it to yourself: Take your pulse without any music on in the background. Now begin playing the music, and notice how your heartbeat matches the speed of the music.

Thus, listening to fast music and trying to relax is like drinking three cups of coffee and trying to fall asleep. I call this the 'audio caffeine' factor.

Another of the great myths that I've helped to explode is that most classical music, especially the now discredited "Mozart effect", is the best choice for relaxation. There are so many reasons why this is not true, but let me share one of the simplest and easily identifiable.

I demonstrate what I've coined the 'scalus interruptus' effect. I sing a familiar pattern of ascending musical tones that we recognize as a scale, a compositional structure basic to most music. The surprise is what happens when I stop on the seventh tone, without finishing the scale. What do you notice? Notice if you're holding your breath.

If you're like most people, you'll be holding your breath, waiting for the other "musical" shoe to drop, waiting for the resolution of that pattern. We've been culturally conditioned to expect that. Unconsciously, we are anticipating where the music will go in the future, and that creates stress.

Indeed, you can only relax in the 'present' moment. You can't relax in the future. Therefore, music that activates this mental analysis makes it impossible to quiet the mind, and adds to your stress level, rather than diminishing it.

This holds true for harmonic progressions as well. More difficult to notice at first, but identified by Dr. John Diamond and proven with behavioral kinesiology, are the more subtle energetic factors related to intention and the physical, emotional and spiritual condition of the musician. I coined the phrase "music is a carrier wave of consciousness" in 1976 to describe how this might occur.

A growing sector of healing music now incorporates brainwave entrainment tones to further enhance the desired effects of helping the listener dial in specific frequencies of alpha, theta or delta brainwave activity for heightened relaxation, healing, and meditation.

I encourage you to explore the wide world of sound healing for yourself. It's still legal, inexpensive and energy-renewable. You'll want to add these healing resources to your own 'sound medicine library'. And remember, it's so easy to benefit, even if you only have five minutes to 'treat' yourself. All you have to do is listen.

CHAPTER 16

Mahendra Kumar Trivedi

Beginnings

I was born in 1963 in a small town in central India. I grew up in a traditional Hindu family, but I always felt very different from my parents and my brother and sister. As a small boy I thought someone must have kidnapped me from my real family because there was no connection there at all. I was very lonely and spent a lot of time alone, but I felt my life had some higher purpose beyond the dogma and traditions my family followed.

After I graduated from high school, my father insisted I go to engineering college, so I did and received a degree from a good school. Later, I began working as a mechanical engineer at a very respected engineering firm and, from all outward appearances, I seemed to be leading a normal everyday life.

But still I was not happy. I did not care about my work, and found no joy in it because I was not following my life's purpose. Even from childhood I had special abilities, such as a photographic memory and deep abilities of perception. And as I went about my life, not caring about my work, these abilities continued to grow stronger.

Then one night in November of 1995, I was gifted by the Divine. I received the instruction that I should leave everything, and go out into the world, and use my unique gifts to help the people. I did not question or hesitate. Immediately I left my job, my family, and everything that was familiar to me, and went out to find the people of my destiny.

I have always trusted the Divine and the guidance It gives me. I am devoted to it and follow the instructions I receive, no question. It is like taking the route the GPS in the car tells you to take. You do not question, you just trust and follow its instruction, and you get where you are meant to go. As long as I follow the instructions of my Divine, my abilities will remain with me. And the power of this divine energy I transmit will continue to grow. Really, it has been getting more powerful all the time.

One of the most important instructions I have received is to go for the scientific proof that this energy works. The science is most important to me because it shows without question what this energy can do. In more than 4,000 studies and scientific experiments of every kind, done at some of the most respected research facilities in the world, we have seen the effect this energy has on plants, animals, humans, and even on non-living materials such as metals, polymers and ceramics, etc. We call this the Trivedi Effect®.

Anyone can claim they are a healer or that they can do some kind of magic. But we must see the proof in a legitimate scientific laboratory. Most people who make these claims have no real abilities or they are using trickery. This is what magic is - trickery. There is magic and then there are miracles.

The miraculous is that which truly creates transformation. A magic trick begins and ends. But there is no end to the miracle of transformation. It goes on and on, no beginning and no ending. This is what this divine energy does; it creates transformation, even at the cellular level. We have done conclusive research that proves this is the case.

My interest in science is for this reason. I want to know what can the Trivedi Effect® accomplish? We need the empirical evidence to show what this energy can do; what kind of transformation it can bring.

Up till now there has been no empirical evidence to back up the claims of the healers and gurus. All we have are the studies on the placebo effect and the personal testimonies of the people. There has been fakery or trickery, or lying to the people.

So for this reason most people in the world may find it hard to believe that this energy that I transmit can really change material conditions. They cannot readily believe that the laws of nature can be overturned.

But this is the power of the Divine. This is the power of this energy. It is not me who is doing it. I am just the conduit. Most people are skeptical at first, and it is good to be skeptical. I am always unsure of what the results will be before I try a new experiment, or do a new study. But once the irrefutable evidence is produced, being skeptical becomes stupidity.

People always have questions. They want to know why and how this can be. They doubt and think it might be trickery. But the evidence shows what is true transformation. This energy is unlimited in the good it can do. If we connect to it, the potential for human life is also unlimited. But in human life we always have limits, so the people are slow to accept the possibility of limitless good.

So for this reason, I chose to research the effects of this energy on plants and non-living materials first. With plants or polymers, there will be no questions or doubts. There will also be no placebo effect. There is no mind to get into it. The results just happen.

In humans, the mind has a role, which is why the placebo effect produces some results in certain cases. It becomes more complicated with the people, but we still see many dramatic results, which are validated by the science.

This energy is *so* powerful. Its potential to bring happiness is unlimited because it connects the people to their own inner guidance system. And when a person is truly connected, the divine "blueprint" for his or her life is restored and every part of life is naturally fulfilled.

Today the fact that a close relationship exists between the mind and the body is well accepted. What goes on in one affects the other. If there are disturbances in the mind, the harmony of the body can be disrupted.

The mind and body are an extension of the soul and the spirit. Soul is the source of infinite energy, and your spirit is what connects the soul to your mind and body. If you are disconnected from the soul, your body and mind will suffer. But just understanding this doesn't strengthen the connection, except in the sense that it might motivate a person to find a way to get connected.

This is the great value of these energy transmissions; they strengthen the connection between soul, spirit, mind, and body so you can live according to your own divinely designed blueprint. When all the people are living in this state of being connected, we will have the kind of world everyone is seeking.

We do not need to understand how this energy works to bring about transformation. Right now the scientists have no understanding of it. Current science is working to solve all kinds of human problems, but without this understanding, it is also causing more problems such as drug side effects, genetic engineering, and much more.

This energy has the ability to rectify all that. The Trivedi Effect® seems to result in "miraculous" occurrences that can't be explained by current science—crop yields dramatically increase without the use of fertilizers or pesticides; microbes evolve; but as understanding comes, we will break through to a new scientific paradigm.

Benjamin Franklin harnessed the energy of lightning, which gave the world electricity. Today we cannot imagine living without electricity. In the same way, this energy from the Divine will transform human experience, and the world itself, and usher in this new science.

But for right now, all we need to understand is that human potential is unlimited. You do not have to "believe in" this energy to receive its benefits. It works whether you believe in it or not. Humans have the unique ability to resist as well as consciously accept ideas.

However, mental resistance can reduce the energy's conductivity. When thought is clear and open, there is more receptivity. The energy works better and flows more effortlessly when there is no resistance. It is like the frictionless flow that quantum physicists talk about.

This is why the Trivedi Effect® in plants, animals, and non-living materials is so powerful and dramatic—because they have no mental resistance to the energy.

CHAPTER 17

Brian David Andersen

Withdrawing From the Business of Disease

In the late 1990s, scientists made the greatest discovery in human health when they detected, discovered, probed and analyzed a thin sheath of phosphorous that covers all cells of plants, animals and humans. The composition of the phosphorous sheaths includes vortex or wormhole-like configurations that speed up and slow down light particles transferring in and out of the core of our cells. Knowledge of and harnessing the power in the phosphorous-based sheaths is a key step to withdrawing from the business of disease.

Raw materials and molecules of the chemical elements in water, food, vitamins, minerals and nutrients DO NOT penetrate or absorb into our cells via the phosphorous sheaths enveloping our cells. Only light particles in the molecules of the chemical elements are allowed to transfer into our cells. Humans, animals and plants only transmit light particles and waves in and out of our cells. The base and fundamental purposes of humans, animals and plants are to absorb and emit light particles that are normally contained with the molecules of the chemical elements.

A sheath of phosphorous also covers the entire nervous system of animals and humans. The DNA helix is composed of mostly phosphorous and the critical chemical element in the mitochondria (energy battery) of an animal or human cell is phosphorous.

When the chemical element of phosphorous is separated from all other chemical elements, is in a pure form and exposed to a normal atmosphere, the phosphorous makes a hissing sound and disappears. The highly energetic phosphorous can only remain in this dimension by compounding with another chemical element. And these phosphoric compounds envelop, and are components for, all plasma membranes of plant, animal and human cells. Numerous private and university microbiology laboratories are investigating the function and significance of the phosphoric compounds in sheaths since they envelop every living biologically-based cell.

The most common chemical element that compounds with phosphorous is oxygen, which remains stable around and in your cells and nervous system.

The chemical element of phosphorous absorbs and transmits light particles, and we call that state 'phosphorescence'. Our whole existence, whether human, animal or plant experiences - are the transfer and movement of light particles via the phosphorous located in key and critical locations in us. The phosphorous sheaths also regulate the amount of light particles and waves flowing in and out of the cells. All human and animal cells are composed of the same simple chemical elements.

Based upon 20 years of investigation and discovery, this scientific researcher/inventor and commentator in the documentary *The Business of Disease* feels and believes the phosphoric sheaths covering all cells, and the phosphoric compounds in and around the plasma membranes of cells in plants, animals and humans, function as chemical, electromagnetic and scalar wave filters and regulators. The hardware of our cells (phosphorous compounds) are the basis and foundation for all biological entities to function in and interact with both the intuitive and psychotronic realm of this and other multi-dimensions.

Water Hydration

Youth, energy and vitality are achieved and maintained by hydrating your cells with the most true and simplest compound of the universe – water. The secondary, auxiliary and peripheral function of water (H_2O) is to transfer minerals and nutrients to the cells of humans, animals and plants. The primary and most important *function* of water is to hydrate the cells of humans, animals and plants with the two chemical elements in water – Hydrogen and Oxygen. The key to proper hydration is that all of the water molecules are absorbed and assimilated into all of your cells. Any chemical element other that Hydrogen and Oxygen in potable drinking water is most often rejected by the Phosphorous sheaths surrounding our cells.

The moment to moment and specific function of the Phosphoric chemical filter of each cell is to allow only the light particles (ions) in Hydrogen and Oxygen to enter and hydrate (stimulate and organize) the other chemical elements in the cells. The only chemical elements allowed into our cells on a continuous basis by the Phosphorous sheaths are Hydrogen and Oxygen.

The absorption of light particles of chemical elements other than Hydrogen and Oxygen are regulated when our Phosphorous sheaths are functioning properly. For example, each cell of the human body has a Potassium/Sodium "pump" and the interaction of these two chemical elements must remain at a critical balance and level. The Phosphoric filter around the cell will only allow light particles of Potassium or Sodium to pass through into the cells if the levels of the "pump" are out of balance.

The best source and means for Potassium and Sodium which will allow light particles of these critical chemical elements to pass through the Phosphorous sheaths are food nutrients. The worst source and means for Potassium, Sodium or any other chemical element in minerals, vitamins and nutrients to pass through the

Phosphorous sheaths are potable drinking waters. As the Phosphorous sheath also rejects the unwanted or unneeded chemical elements in your non-pure drinking water, the critical Hydrogen and Oxygen light particles are also rejected. When this happens the doorways shut and reject all chemical elements thus your drinking non-pure water inhibits absorption and promotes the most devastating condition and the basis for all diseases...dehydration.

The pH level (acid or alkaline) of the light particles in the hydrogen and oxygen in water does not matter, because as the hydrogen and oxygen are passed through the phosphoric filter, they become balanced so that their light particles will work in harmony with the other chemical elements in the cell. The key and only characteristics the phosphoric filter requires for full and complete passage and absorption into the cell is that other chemical elements (contaminants) are not present in the water being absorbed, and the light particles in the hydrogen and oxygen have the proper or coherent molecular organization. I have found that distilled water treated by the *Tri-Vortex Technology* items has a balanced pH level and is in a highly permeable state. Therefore, the pH of distilled water rises to the exact level of the individual when consumed.

As our civilization propels into the early 21st century there are numerous individuals, groups and corporations researching or selling water that promote the misconception that the primary function of water is to transfer minerals into the body. Persons believing or influenced by these illogical theories and directions about the primary function of water therefore mistakenly conclude that water with minerals or "clusters" and/or at a certain pH level provides optimum health, vitality anti-aging and release from diseases. These same individuals, groups and corporations do not understand the value and purpose of pure water with only the essential chemical elements of Hydrogen and Oxygen present in the liquid regardless of the pH level. Also, many of these same groups have misdirected and muddled the primary function of water by over emphasizing the importance of the pH levels.

Nature's Distillation Process

Pure waters with only the chemical elements of Hydrogen and Oxygen are generated by the Earth's atmosphere every day. The weather components and dynamics of planet Earth provides a form of distillation by creating low temperatures and low heat on the Earth's surface that evaporates ground and sea water. As the evaporated water molecules accumulate in clouds, only the chemical elements of Hydrogen or Oxygen are gathered and levitated in the sky. Nature's primary method of providing water to plants, animals and humans is a low temperature distillation process. The precious and sterile airborne liquid vapors are transported by clouds and so the pure distilled water molecules can be deposited at sea and on land Any farmer growing agriculture crops prefers fresh, pure living and distilled rainwater to hydrate their crops rather than dead irrigation water.

The difference between the fresh pure rain water with acid pH and the irrigation water is that the rain water is composed of only Hydrogen and Oxygen and the molecules made from those chemical elements are structured in a coherent and organized manner. In contrast, the irrigation water with an acid or alkaline pH level is contaminated with other chemical elements such as Sodium and minerals and the molecules made from the chemical elements of the irrigation water are disorganized and moving in a chaotic manner.

An Entire Civilization Impacted By Pure & Structured Water

Before European explorers discovered the island civilizations of the Pacific Ocean in the late 1700s, one tribe stood-out as being bigger, stronger, more intelligent, motivated and leaders of the pack. This special tribe was situated on the western portion of the Big Island of Hawaii. The volcanic activity of the Big Island creates special kinds of tubes that move lava underground before forcing the hot molten substance to the surface and into the ocean. Transferring hot magma via tubes to the surface is a far less violent method than the eruptive blasts of ancient Pompey and Mount St. Helen's. This gentle method of moving magma created a great benefit for humans.

Eventually the hot lava ceases to flow but the tubes remain intact and absent of any lava therefore hollow caves with fresh air are created. The lava tubes are primarily made of various kinds of iron oxides. The middle layers of the iron oxides are subjected to pressure created by the sheer weight of the upper layers and the containing lower layers. Tree roots slithered their way down the cracks and gaps of the molten lava that transports water droplets into the caves.

In 1992, I subjected one end of plastic tube filled with a mixture of iron oxides and other compounds to very high voltages created by a powerful Tesla Coil. The inspiration to subject iron oxides to Tesla Coil high voltages came from a metal foundry in China. Workers exposed to furnaces melting iron oxides were stronger, healthier, more intelligent and lived longer than the normal Chinese citizen. Chinese inventors created a medical device using a heat generating disk that is covered with iron oxides. This pricey medical device is sold under various names around the world.

But instead of using metal disks and heat, I used a plastic tube and high voltages. A copper wire was placed into the mixture at the opposite end of the plastic tube with the high voltages. The wire was then connected to four-inch square copper metal plate. Nine minutes after any solid or liquid was placed on the copper plate, the smell and taste of the liquid or solid was dramatically improved. Also human pain, fatigue and soreness were relieved by the copper plate.

I concluded the high voltages were not responsible for **The Field** but the electromagnetic frequency created within the high voltage was responsible for **The Field**. After several attempts of transmitting various signals from a frequency generator through the iron oxide mixture, a special waveform created a **more powerful field** than the high voltage Tesla Coil and the costly Chinese heat disk medical device.

What the Chinese inventors accomplished with heat and iron oxides and I accomplished with frequency and iron oxides, nature creates a coherent electromagnetic field by subjecting the iron oxides to pressure. The pressurized iron oxides of the cooled volcanic lava generate a one-of-a-kind coherent electromagnetic field. However, the high pressure forges cracks and crevices in the iron oxides thus creating pathways for surface water to trickle into the lava caves. The iron oxides are so fractured that roots from plants on the surface jut through and hang from the ceilings of lava caves. The waters flowing through the coherent electromagnetic fields of the iron oxides take on the same identical organized structure due to the force known as sympathetic resonance.

I explored the *Kula Kai Caverns* on the down slope of Mauna Loa near South Point on the Big Island of Hawaii in October of 2008. Before starting the lava cave tour, I did not know the lava caves were made from iron oxides nor was he aware of the history of the local population. Due to his extensive experimentations and successes with iron oxides, half way through his exploration of the lava caves I stated the one-of-a-kind waters must have created a special breed of human living on the western portion of the Big Island of the Hawaii. I predicted the residents drinking the water were stronger more intelligent and lived longer than residents living on the Eastern side of the Big Island and all other island cultures of the Pacific Ocean.

Guide Kathlyn Richardson concurred with my conclusions based upon researched historical facts, evidence, data and documents. Only one tribe residing on any island culture of the Pacific Ocean made the effort to build gourd pots to complete the arduous task of collecting the coherent waters dripping in the dark treacherous lava caves. In her book, *The Polynesian Family System of Ka'u,* author Mary Kawena Pukui details the unique, rugged and independent peoples of Ka'u living on western edge of the Big Island. This population produced the ruling class of the Hawaiian Islands

I am the first researcher to connect how and why the structured iron oxide waters of the lava caves positively shaped and influenced the novel local Hawaiian human population. Regretfully, the sterling local natives stopped collecting and drinking the lava cave waters shortly after the arrival of Europeans settlers in the mid-1800s.

However, I desired a simple and faster method to improve the molecular structure of water and pressed on with additional research and development. Does one have to travel to the caves of the Hawaii to secure fresh, pure and structured water? No!

Coherent Molecular Structure

The *Tri-Vortex Technology* products create coherent molecular structure in any liquid to the same level as fresh cut carrot juice is available for purchase. The *Tri-Vortex Technology* products transforms high or low temperature distilled water from being the very worst for the human body to the very best for the human body. Operating the *Tri-Vortex Technology* products are very simple. All one has to do to create the proper coherent molecular structure in any liquid with any kind of pH level or any amount of minerals or clusters is to place the container with the liquid on or adjacent to the *Tri-Vortex Technology* product for 10 to 30 seconds.

The chemical elements in plants, animals and humans are the same but the molecules are arranged in various and different manners that manifest into divergent life forms. Therefore, the flower test results can be extrapolated so the individual can conclude that structured distilled water also has benefits for animals and humans.

What You and Your Family Can Drink Today

Store bought distilled water in plastic bottles can be transformed into a very good source of hydration. The plastic containers for distilled are the cheapest kinds of plastic on the market and constantly de-gas or emit unwanted chemicals in the water. However, the chemicals are in a gas form and can be released from the distilled water. The cheap plastic of distilled water containers are inappropriate so what kind of containers are appropriate?

Common plastic used for the cheap distilled water bottles and drinking containers are based upon petrochemicals. The chemical elements and compounds in petroleum based water containers are unstable and leach into any liquid. Polycarbonate containers are based upon, surprise, carbon, but also include a substance known as Bisphenol -A that has been proven to cause numerous negative health conditions especially in female reproductive organs.

A 47-year old female began drinking distilled water contained in polycarbonate bottles on a daily basis for the first time in late 2006. She was also drinking a minimum of one can of carbonated cola per day. During the summer of 2007 the female exhibited classical negative health problems associated with clinical studies involved in investigating Bisphenol -A including lumps in and hardening of the breast and uterine related issues. All polycarbonate containers were immediately replaced with stainless steel and the female was treated with activated charcoal poultices on the breast and uterus. The female also eliminated the carbonated colas from her diet. The female also orally took the activated charcoal to absorb and remove the harmful Bisphenol - A. By the winter of 2007, all symptoms related to the Bisphenol -A contamination totally disappeared with no negative side or after effects. **The only containers one must have for maximum hydration with total safety are glass, ceramic and stainless steel.**

Mineral, spring, well and filtered waters having any pH level with molecular chaos have a tendency to dull the senses of smell and taste and deadens the nerve fibers in the digestive passages in the throat of an individual. Degassed store bought distilled water treated by the *Tri-Vortex Technology* stimulates the senses of smell and taste and enlivens the nerve fibers in the digestive passages in the throat.

Sustaining a deadly level of dehydration is a sure way to continue to support the business of disease. The human being functions no differently than a high performance race car. Would anyone in their right mind put regular gasoline into a Ferrari engine? No. But humans pour substandard liquids into their high performance bodies every day and by default are the participants in the ongoing business of disease. The traditional medical establishment sells the business of disease by omitting the importance of proper water hydration with pure and structured water. Do you want to continue to be a victim of these proprietors? If your response is no then the answer to solving the problems created by the business of disease is to no longer be a dumb downed and uninformed buyer in this racket. The business of disease will then cease to be a viable entity when the customers withdraw from buying into the useless and harmful products and services.

Footnotes

Chapter 5

Dobrian, C. (1992). Music and Language. *Music.arts.uci.edu*.
    Retrieved February 17, 2014, from
    http://music.arts.uci.edu/dobrian/CD.music.lang.htm.

Scientist Prove DNA Can Be Reprogrammed. (2013).
    ScienceGymnasium. Retrieved February 17, 2014 from
    http://www.sciencegymnasium.com/2013/07/scientist-
    prove-dna-can-be-reprogrammed.html#more.

Wheeler, M. (2004, February). Signal Discovery?. *Smithsonian.com*.
    Retrieved February 17, 2014, from
    http://www.smithsonianmag.com/science-nature/signal-
    discovery-104663195/.

Chapter 7

[1] Rossi, E., Erickson-Klein, R., Rossi, K. (2008-2012). *Collected
    Works of Milton H. Erickson Volumes* 1–10). Phoenix, AZ:
    Milton H. Erickson Press.

[2] Rossi, E., Rossi, K. (Ed). (2012). *Creating Consciousness: How
    Therapists Can Facilitate Wonder, Wisdom, Truth & Beauty*.
    Phoenix, AZ: Milton H. Erickson Press.

[3] Lawson, L. (2014). Lee Lawson. Retrieved from
www.leelawson.com

[4] Oliver, D. Oliver, C. H. (2014). Dave's AstangaYoga. Retrieved
    from www.DavesAstangaYoga.com

Chapter 8

[1] Rossi, E. (1972/1985/2000). *Dreams, Consciousness, Spirit,* 3rd Edition. Phoenix: Zeig, Tucker, Theisen.

[2]Rossi, E. (2007). *The Breakout Heuristic: The New Neuroscience of Mirror Neurons, Consciousness and Creativity in Human Relationships: Vol. 1, Selected Papers of Ernest Lawrence Rossi.* Phoenix, Arizona: The Milton H. Erickson Foundation Press.

[2] Rossi, E. (2012). *Creating Consciousness: How Therapists Can Facilitate Wonder, Wisdom, Truth and Beauty: Vol. 2 Selected Papers of Ernest Lawrence Rossi.* Phoenix: Arizona: The Milton H. Erickson Foundation Press.

Contributing Authors

Romeo Brooks PhD: As a retired Firefighter and Emergency Medical Technician (EMT) for over 32 years, Dr. Romeo Brooks has seen an overwhelming amount of unnecessary pain and suffering. His quest for knowledge in the field of health was initiated after his father passed from emphysema and his mother from a blocked intestine and kidney failure. As a result Dr. Brooks studied to become an Iridologist, Natural Hygienist, Herbalist and earned a Ph.D. in Naturopathic Medicine. He also created a line of extraordinary natural wellness products through Roots Nutrition and Fitness in Inglewood, CA. Dr. Brooks is married to the lovely Mai Brooks and they have four children.

www.rootsnutrition.com

Ann Boroch: Ann Boroch is a certified nutritional consultant, naturopath, certified clinical hypnotherapist, author, and inspirational speaker. She healed herself from multiple sclerosis and has been symptom-free for 20 years. Ann specializes in allergies, autoimmune diseases, and gastrointestinal and endocrine disorders, and is an expert on candida. Her successful practice of 15 years in Los Angeles, California, has helped thousands of clients achieve optimum health. Ann has appeared on national radio and television, including a featured appearance on The Montel Williams Show, where she promoted her breakthrough book *Healing Multiple Sclerosis*. Her latest book is *The Candida Cure: The 90-Day Program to Beat Candida and Restore Vibrant Health*.

www.annboroch.com

Dr. Bradley Nelson: Dr. Bradley Nelson graduated in 1988 with honors from Life Chiropractic College West in San Lorenzo, California. He has lectured internationally on the natural healing of chronic illness, and was in private practice until 2004, successfully treating patients from across the US and Canada who were suffering from Chronic Fatigue Syndrome, Fibromyalgia and a wide variety of other chronic ailments. A holistic chiropractic physician and medical intuitive, Dr. Nelson is one of the world's foremost experts in the emerging fields of bioenergetic medicine and energy psychology.

www.drbradleynelson.com

Dorothy M. Neddermeyer, PhD: Dorothy M. Neddermeyer, PhD is an internationally recognized authority on bridging Science, Spirit and Human Potential. She has over 30 years of experience as a healing facilitator, speaker, and educator in natural health and wellness; and personal/professional development.

Dr. Dorothy is Founder/CEO of Genesis Consultants, dedicated to holistic healing and personal development. She is Immediate Past President, International Association for Regression Research and Therapies. She serves on the board for Arizona Holistic Chamber of Commerce, and is Board Advisor for the 4th World Regression Congress and a lifetime member of National Registry of Who's Who.

www.gen-assist.com

Sharry Edwards: Sharry Edwards has been accused of being too scientific by some, too esoteric by others. In actuality she is a bridge between both fields of inquiry. Her unique auditory abilities allow her to "hear" each person's Signature Sound and that ability led to serious questions about what those sounds could possibly mean. She has been tested in many labs and still uses her toning abilities to work with people who have no voice. Her curiosity and her need to make a difference in the world led her to develop a scientific format for computational biology using the sounds of the human voice.

Sharry calls this new field of discovery Sonoistry. Just as we have a system of basic elements that we call chemistry, there is a basic set of sounds/frequencies that can monitor, predict and manage biological function. String theory found a basis for the existence of DNA; Sonoistry is the basic system for RNA. (DNA is the pattern; RNA maintains the pattern.) Sharry is the acknowledged pioneer in the emerging field of Human BioAcoustic Vocal Profiling. She has for many years provided the leading edge research to show the voice as a holographic representation of the body.

www.soundhealthoptions.com/nutrasounds/

Bradley York Bartholomew: Bradley York Bartholomew has written several articles on Hindu philosophy that were published in various philosophical journals in India in the early 1990s. In 2004 he came across the theory of Fosar & Bludorf about The Networked Intelligence in the DNA, and he realized that this networked intelligence in the DNA equates with what the Hindus call Brahman or the Universal Consciousness. Then came the discoveries about memristors that are capable of both storing and processing data in biological computers, which means that the Universe could be in the nature of processed data. If this is the case, we literally do live in the mind of God.

The author is currently a full-time student in Physics and Genetics at Griifith University, Gold Coast, Australia. His book:

THE SPIRITUAL GENOME: This eBook contains fascinating new discoveries about memristors in the DNA. Memristors work on the model of biological computers like the human brain. Memristors have memory storage and processing ability, and are being developed for computer hardware.

www.spiritualgenome.com

Kathryn L. Rossi Ph.D.: Kathryn L. Rossi Ph.D is a Founding Director of the Milton H. Erickson Institute of the California Central Coast (MHE-CCC). She has edited, authored or co-authored more than 15 books and 25 scientific articles.

Along with Ernest Rossi and Roxanna Erickson Klein, she received the 2008 Hilgard Award for Best Theoretical Paper: *The Future Orientation of Constructive Memory: An Evolutionary Perspective on Therapeutic Hypnosis and Brief Psychotherapy.*

Dr. Rossi is a Professor at the Neuroscience Institute for Psychotherapists of Solopaca, Italy, and Chief Financial Officer (CFO) and Vice President for The Ernest Lawrence Rossi Non-Profit Foundation for Psychosocial Genomics Research. She is a board member for the Erickson Foundation Archives and Press in Phoenix, Arizona and is an Advisory Board Member of The Simonton Cancer Center.

Dr. Rossi casts a wide net of in-depth studies in the fields of psychology, therapeutic hypnosis, neuroscience, art, music and yoga. Her current areas of interest are how to integrate yoga, art, beauty and truth into creating new consciousness on a psychosocial genomic level. She is a registered Yoga teacher (RYT 500).

A psychologist in private practice in Los Osos, California, Dr. Kathryn Rossi also conducts workshops and consultations internationally as well as through Skype and other Internet video-activated (VoIP) services.

www.ernestrossi.com/kathrynrossi

Ernest Rossi, Ph.D.: Ernest Rossi, Ph.D. is an internationally recognized psychotherapist and expert on creativity and mind-body healing. He is the author of 36 books and over 170 research papers published in many languages. Dr. Rossi's writing and research describe advances in creative work, therapeutic hypnosis, psychoneuroimmunology, and the experiential dimensions of healing. He is widely recognized for his inspiring and insightful presentations. Nurses, psychologists, coaches, and allied health professionals applaud his wealth of practical information, and his ability to describe key concepts with eloquence and warmth. His most recent books are Creating Consciousness, (2011, In Press), Ultradian Rhythms from Molecule to Mind: A New Vision of Life (Co-edited with David Lloyd, Springer, 2008), The Breakout Heuristic (Milton H. Erickson Foundation Press, 2007), The Psychobiology of Gene Expression: Neuroscience and Neurogenesis in Hypnosis and the Healing Arts (W. W. Norton, 2002) and A Dialogue with Our Genes: The Psychosocial Genomics of Therapeutic Hypnosis and Psychotherapy (Zeig-Tucker-Theisen, 2004). He recently updated CDs of the New Neuroscience Edition of Collected Papers of Milton H. Erickson and a dozen other books co-authored with him.

www.ernestrossi.com

Amit Goswami Ph.D: Professor of physics at the University of Oregon's Institute of Theoretical Science for over 30 years, (now retired) Dr. Goswami is a revolutionary in a growing body of renegade scientists who, in recent years, have ventured into the domain of the spiritual in an attempt both to interpret the seemingly inexplicable findings of their experiments, and to validate their intuitions about the existence of a spiritual dimension of life.

A prolific writer, teacher and visionary, Dr. Goswami has appeared in the movie "What the Bleep do We know?", The "Dalai Lama Renaissance", and the recently released award-winning documentary "The Quantum Activist."

www.amitgoswami.org/

Dr. Jacob Liberman: Dr. Jacob Liberman received a Doctorate of Optometry in 1973 from Southern College of Optometry, a Ph.D. in Vision Science in 1986 from The College of Syntonic Optometry. Dr. Liberman's first book, *Light: Medicine of the Future*, established him as an authority in the field of light and color therapy and is considered a classic in its field. His second book, *Take Off Your Glasses and See*, was inspired by the miraculous healing of his own vision, and offers a radically new approach to restoring and enhancing one's vision naturally. His latest book, *Wisdom From an Empty Mind*, is a compilation of one-page essays on light, vision and consciousness. All three books have received international acclaim and have been published in multiple languages.

For the past 35 years, Dr. Liberman has worked with thousands of individuals, ranging from children with learning difficulties to Olympic and professional athletes. His work has been enthusiastically endorsed by luminaries in the fields of science, medicine, consciousness and professional sports.

In 2001, Dr. Liberman founded Exercise Your Eyes, Inc. and invented the EYEPORT Vision Training System. The EYEPORT represents years of clinical research and integrates Dr. Liberman's pioneering discoveries in vision science into the first FDA-cleared medical device of its kind available to the public.

www.exerciseyoureyes.com/

Dr. G. Clotaire Rapaille: Dr. G. Clotaire Rapaille is an internationally known expert in Archetype Discoveries and Creativity. His unique approach to marketing combines a psychiatrist's depth of analysis with a businessman's attention to practical concerns. He has written more than ten books on these topics. One of his books, Creative Communication, has become the standard reference for the French advertising industry. He is a sought-after lecturer on creativity and communication.

Dr. Rapaille's technique for market research has grown out of his work in the areas of psychiatry, psychology, and cultural anthropology. His work is an extension of the work done by many of the great scholars of the 20th century, including Jung, Laing, Levi-Strauss and Ruth Benedict.

Dr. Rapaille's world travels, a term in the diplomatic corps, and extensive marketing research on product archetypes for international corporations, have given him a fresh perspective on American business and American society.

www.archetypediscoveriesworldwide.com/

Patricia Bisch: *Freedom from Food* presents a revolutionary program designed by Patricia Bisch, who discovered the secret to regaining her power over food without deprivation. Built on the solid foundation of quantum physics, which substantiates how the mind affects the body, it provides practical applications of principles that guide you to making your consciousness strong enough to transform your body.

Patricia Bisch, MA, MFT, lived the painful life of an overeater from her teen years to well into early adulthood. Then, over 30 years ago, she discovered the secret to regaining her power over food – not through deprivation, but as a way to enjoy eating and to lose weight anyway.

She proceeded to practice and perfect the principles she writes about, and today, she remains completely healed. In addition to reaching Master-level proficiency in two energetic healing methods, and maintaining a private practice in psychotherapy, specializing in EMDR therapy, Patricia lectures, conducts media appearances and leads classes and workshops on weight loss.

http://patriciabisch.com/

Rita Soman: Rita Soman, originally from New Delhi, India holds a Masters in Psychology and is a Certified Alcohol & Drug Specialist. She currently uses a process called PSYCH-K® that has surpassed all her expectations and those of her clients. It brought very dramatic positive changes in her personal & professional life. With over 30 years of experience as a psychotherapist, Rita finds this process very empowering, effective and easy to use, to reprogram the subconscious mind with positive beliefs. The results are quick and long lasting. It works for almost every problem one may face in life in the areas of, Relationships, Self-Esteem, Spirituality, Health, Prosperity, Personal Power, Grief & Loss and Alcohol & Drug Addiction, etc. PSYCH-K® works very well with other modalities. PSYCH-K® takes one beyond the power of Intention, Visualization, Positive Thinking, Affirmations, and Willpower. It can help people free their mind from the limitations of the past and give them empowerment over their own lives. Change beliefs and change your life. It's that simple!

www.beliefmantra.com/

Sonia Barrett: Sonia Barrett is the Producer of the documentary The Business of Disease. She is the author of *The Holographic Canvas: The Fusing of Mind and Matter* published in September 2008 and her second book, *A Journey of Possibilities* published in 2014. She is also the publisher of the book *Health; An Inside Job an Outside Business*. Sonia Barrett's insights are cutting edge with much of it supported by quantum physics. Her work bridges the gap between science and spirituality in a simplified format. She addresses the programming, beliefs and concepts by which we have lived our lives both individually and collectively.

Through her workshops and lectures Sonia Barrett presents clarity in understanding the paradox of both the real and the unreal; the visible and the invisible components of reality; the holographic experience.

http://www.spiritinform.com/

Steven Halpern: Steven Halpern is an award-winning composer, recording artist and producer whose healing music has helped millions worldwide to experience the blessings and benefits of deep relaxation and inner peace.

CHAKRA SUITE, his debut release in 1975 helped establish a "quiet revolution" and a new genre in contemporary instrumental music. To date it has sold over 700,000 copies. Halpern's cumulative sales exceed 6 million units and his current releases continue to set the standard of excellence in the field.

Based on his own spiritual and health-related experiences, Steven discovered secrets of combining ancient sound healing traditions with quantum biology and energy medicine to produce recordings that support relaxation, stress management, yoga, meditation, massage, sleep, accelerated learning and pure listening pleasure.

Halpern's most representative and best-selling recordings include *PEACE OF MIND, MUSIC FOR SOUND HEALING, INNER PEACE, IN THE OM ZONE* and the Billboard-charting *DEJA-BLUES*.

Mahendra Kumar Trivedi: Mahendra Kumar Trivedi possesses a unique ability to transmit an unknown energy through his thoughts. This energy has the ability to transform all living organisms such as plants, trees, seeds, bacteria, viruses, fungi, animals, cancer cells, human cells...everything, for better performance. In addition, this energy has the ability to transform non-living materials, such as metals, ceramics, polymers, and chemicals, by changing the structure of the atom permanently.

After five years, Mr. Trivedi began to ask why this energy should be limited to humans. He felt that if this energy is real, it must work everywhere, in all things and matter. It must enhance the abilities, properties, and productivity of crops. It must transform bacteria, viruses and fungi; convert cancer cells into non cancer cells; and make metals, chemicals, and polymers stronger.

Due to his skeptical nature, he became engaged in scientific research. With the help of the most sophisticated technology available to science and under controlled conditions, he began to discover and prove this energy's characteristics, behavior, limitations and abilities and its impact on living and non-living things. He understood that if this energy can change the structure of an atom, then nothing is impossible for this energy. He has compiled a remarkable track record of success, including nearly 4,000 well-documented scientific studies on his ability to profoundly affect matter down to the level of the atom.

www.trivedifoundation.org/

Brian David Andersen: Brian David Andersen perfected and harnessed the spiral and spherical tables of the chemical elements. Those discoveries were the foundation to mathematically prove the Great Pyramid in Egypt is a three-sided pyramid built inside of a four-sided pyramid. Geometric and electromagnetic applications from the aforementioned discoveries are the basis for a product line of subtle energy items known as Tri-Vortex Technology.

Andersen was the first to experience and distribute subtle energy items based upon the new and emerging scientific field called Light Particle Assimilation. Brian's stunning successes in the field of Light Particle Assimilation were responsible for his being appointed a Consultant and Scientist specializing in subtle energy and electromagnetic research and applications for the prestigious Hippocrates Health Institute in January of 2012.

www.trivortex.com

Sponsors

PRACTITIONERS/ PRODUCTS & FOOD FOR THOUGHT

Supporting health in Spirit, Mind and Body

- Global Cardio Care
- Regeneration
- Ann Boroch
- Solla Wellness
- Invisible Wellness System
- Harmony Farms
- Creative Chakra
- Conscious Self Care
- Lady of the Lotus

Regeneration

A new Integrative Health platform

Regeneration is an Integrative Health platform created by a team of leading Naturopathic Physicians, Medical Doctors, Researchers and Technologists. Our mission is to provide free access to an ecosystem powered by artificial intelligence that guides and curates personalized health and wellness recommendations for you, your family, and friends.

Regeneration is built on the foundations of Integrative Medicine. Our Ecosystem addresses all aspects of the body, mind, and spirit. Now you can have a one-click connection of your labs, genetic data, wearable sensors, health history, hospital records, and whole body health assessments. All your health data can be connected and protected in your own highly encrypted and HIPAA compliant personal health cloud. Regeneration offers you and your chosen providers the ability to monitor changes and improve your health in real time, 24/7.

Regeneration offers personalized recommendations to improve you and your family's health journey from womb to tomb. Our focus is on prevention, self-care, home health testing, providing online/offline access to trusted doctors and comprehensive Integrative Medicine information and products.

Our Integrative Health Ecosystem offers access to the highest quality professional grade supplements, telehealth consultations with vetted Integrative providers, and complete entry to our

Integrative Medical library. Offering clear guidance and details on all evidence based health and wellness options for you.

Improve your future today by signing up and managing your personalized health dashboard. Enjoy the ability to invite and share your progress with friends, family and physicians.
Forever Free - Begin your Health Journey www.regeneration.com

Maria Whalen

Invisible Wellness System

Why you don't have health freedom

Like most, you probably don't even know what that means!

GUESS WHAT?? Did you know the alternative health industry is NOT the solution?

Want to know WHY almost everyone still has health ailments OR gets a "surprise" diagnosis???

Why you don't have health freedom? Like most, you probably don't even know what that means!

There is a reason why 99% of the hundreds of clients who come to us say that they have tried literally EVERYTHING in the alternative industry, and they are worn out and have lost hope.

There is a reason why tons of health practitioners end up coming to us for help.

There is also a reason why even the people who think they are an expert or claim they know all there is to know about healing the body, still have ailments themselves (some even say I'm only on "one" medicine – as if that shouldn't be alarming!).

You sure you want to know why???

When I healed myself years ago of three rare and seemingly incurable autoimmune diseases, it wasn't the healing myself part that made me want to help people, it was one simple reason... the system that was supposed to heal me in ways that western medicine could not, was also just as broken! After jumping from expert to expert and from one modality to the next, confused and exhausted from "trying" everything and spending thousands and thousands of dollars, I finally took matters into my own hands.

I was shocked and appalled and realized that I must create the very same system for others that I used to heal myself, the Invincible Wellness System.

In many ways my experience was like the ancient parable of the 3 blind men and their first encounter with an elephant...

One encounters the trunk and declares that an elephant is like a big pipe.
One encounters the ear and declares that elephant is like the sturdy sail of a ship.
One encounters the belly and declares the elephant is like a stone wall.

All three had a different experience but they all failed miserably at capturing the totality of an elephant. The alternative medical industry suffers from the same fragmented problem.

We all know that the western system is broken because it is solely focused on illness and disease, and not on healing. And while alternative medicine may offer specific focused improvements, it doesn't actually deliver complete healing and health freedom, either. Both systems keep you dependent, chasing ailments and modalities, and coming back for more.

The most dangerous assumption I hear all the time is when people claim they are healthy or "fine" because either they feel good or because they have done a lot of "health" things like;

- Detoxes, cleanses, or juicing
- Seen countless "practitioners"
- "Healthy" eating or dieting
- Become a Vegan, vegetarian or any title
- Read a book from someone "famous" in health
- Followed a blog or newsletter
- Tried every natural modality
- Relied on supplements, or have miracle "one thing" that has fixed everything, etc.
- Practiced spiritual or energetic medicine
- Used fancy machines
- Trusted the latest big scientific breakthrough or research
- Received normal test results
- Relied on "listening" to their body

But these people DON'T HAVE their own system!

You must have a system in order to achieve "True Health Freedom."

True Health Freedom means YOU take control of your own healing.

That means you know:

- How to heal your body of anything NOW,
- How to NEVER get a surprise diagnosis, and
- How to do it all YOURSELF

A Health Freedom system makes you 100% in control of your health and gives you the remote control to your body.

Without a comprehensive approach that focuses on all the organs and systems that are already there in your body, you will never reach that level of freedom. Focusing on one method, product/supplement, ailment/diagnosis, or an isolated part of the body (like the thyroid) does not give your body what it needs.

There are 5 places (pillars) that the body heals EVERYTHING from. If you don't know how the 5 Pillars interact in your body, what the culprits are in your own life, and what your body is asking for, then you are making some very dangerous assumptions.

You must have a system that gives you full ASSURANCE, so that you never have to use your INSURANCE.

So if you are NOT willing to take full responsibility for your health and fight for your freedom, you will enslave yourself to that/whom which you make responsible for your health.

This isn't rah-rah or woo-woo talk. It's a real, practical and life changing blueprint to empower you, your loved ones, and even your pets!

We don't need more bio-hacks (when did we ever think it was a good idea to hack our body?!).

We don't need more scientific research – if you know how your body works, it already knows what to do!

We need more warriors who know how to care for and heal their OWN bodies, more real health freedom, and more Invincible Wellness!

Are you ready?

Discover the 5 Places (Pillars) your body heals everything from at www.IWSBOOK.com

Solla Puzzido

Her Story

Practical Evolution

"There's a MOVEMENT occurring of tremendous POSITIVE CHANGE and its potency stirs my entire being in euphoric dimensions.

It is the collective force of US, and our 'tribe' of leaders IGNITING, MOLDING, contributing to practical evolutionary awareness to modern day human sexuality.

The works presented resonates so **emphatically** with our true inner selves.

Life radiates through many forms of artistic expression, emotions, feelings, deep resonance with humanistic endeavors..

Sexuality IS part of this realm.

Artistry in Sexual expression can be realized when people are able to rediscover total surrender, trust, and openness.

FEEL the POTENCY

FEEL the POWER

I invite you brothers and sisters to hold hands globally and join in on this incredible Life Force exploration.

Namaste, honoring your heart to mine"

Solla Pizzuto

In the process of the beautiful emergence of life, there is Energy. Every human being came into being from this massive chain reaction of explosive Sexual Energy. This life force energy that runs through our bodies from birth has many references; "chi" in China, "ki" in Japan, and "prana" in India.

Cultivating a healthy Life Force Prana can be referenced as an antidote to prevent disease, degeneration, and ailments. This is my personal journey and my quest for continued mind, body, emotional, spiritual nourishment and age defying longevity practices.

My whole life has been centered in a rich traditional Asian culture and Chinese medicine. I was blessed to grow up nourished with home brewed Chinese Herbs for remedies and prevention. I cannot recall becoming sick nor had I ever seen a day in my childhood of medications. My dear grandmother would prepare the family with the darkest brew of concentrated blends of raw Chinese herbs- all fresh from the local Chinese Medicine doctor. It was also customary for children to massage the parents with bare foot acupressure or with fingers to the body. My parents worked laboriously long hours and often came home exhausted. It was a joy to nurture their tired bodies with a walk along their back.

Since then, my feet have walked the path of the Tao. In flowing with life, it seems the path was all laid out before me and I simply chose to follow my natural nurturing instinct and heart. To attain inner fulfillment in the midst and challenges of everyday life processes, I discovered the freedom, surrender, and embrace of a harmonious way of being.

My background in science, medicine, psychology, health, nutrition, and a multitude of extensive therapeutic bodywork (including Chi Nei Tsang-Kar Sai) plus clinical patient care, all became the ideal ingredients to season my holistic healthcare practices. This has allowed me to have a deeper impact on the people and community I work with.

It is my absolute joy to share the knowledge of cultivating Holistic care- mind, body, spirit, sexuality-- through the embrace and Tao~Healing Love Tantra practices of Life Force Chi- Prana.

Solla Pizzuto, Global Wellness Tao and Healing Love Connections Educator

www.sollawellness.com

Sara Soulati

CEO, Global Cardio Care, Inc.

Changing the Healthcare Paradigm from Illness to Preventive Medicine

Cardiovascular disease is the number one cause of death in the world. Due to the U.S. Food and Drug Administration (FDA) and the structure of the healthcare system, we face looming challenges in cardiovascular disease treatment.

This is how the trouble starts:

- The FDA approves foods that promote cardiovascular disease risk factors. High blood pressure, diabetes, obesity and high cholesterol are diseases that come from food.

- With many high risk factors you end up in the doctor's office.

- The doctor prescribes medication to lower blood pressure, cholesterol and blood sugar levels.

- The medicines are necessary to keep you safe, but the doctor expects you to actually change your lifestyle.

Cardiovascular disease is not a genetic disease. It is a lifestyle disease!

Look at all the food you've been eating -- animal byproducts, processed foods, corn, soy, genetically modified foods, white carbohydrates, and refined sugars. These foods are major contributors to cardiovascular disease. If cardiovascular disease is not genetic, then we must target the foods we have been ingesting over generations.

Families eat the same foods, and that's why diseases run in families, like diabetes, high cholesterol, high blood pressure or heart disease. This pattern continues through life until eventually you develop coronary artery disease.

Coronary Artery Disease

Heart attacks are the leading cause of death in the United States due to blockages of the arteries of the heart.

Coronary artery disease is due to inflammation and poor circulation.

If you've spent a lifetime eating the same foods your parents and grandparents did, you will become a candidate for coronary angioplasty and, likely, a stent. Without a change to lifestyle, you may require open-heart surgery.

Coronary artery bypass surgery is the biggest moneymaker in the United States. They take the vein from your legs, crack open your chest and bypass the blocked artery with a vein from your legs. Eventually, there could be another heart attack, and you can go into heart failure.

Cardiovascular Disease is Preventable

My name is Sara Soulati, creator of the patent-pending Sara Soulati® Health for Life™ program. http://globalcardiocare.com/sara-soulati-health-for-life-program/ I have been working since 1996 to prevent and reverse cardiovascular disease. I am the leading authority of an amazing, powerful, effective treatment called Enhanced External Counterpulsation (EECP®).

Get Squeezed® for Life!

EECP is an FDA-cleared treatment that is safe and effective with no medication or surgery. You lie on a comfortable bed with three blood-pressure-type cuffs wrapped around calves, thighs and buttocks. To the rhythm of your heart, the blood pressure cuffs squeeze blood from the legs and circulate it throughout the body.

As this pumping mechanism circulates oxygenated blood through all organs, EECP helps the body grow new arteries or collaterals, called angiogenesis. Vascular endothelial growth factor, a hormone, is secreted enabling this natural bypass.

I've treated thousands of patients; some had severe chest pain, shortness of breath, poor circulation, heart attack, stroke, enlarged hearts, or congestive heart failure and many were inoperable or elected to forego heart bypass surgery.

Each had EECP a minimum of one hour daily for 35 sessions as part of the Sara Soulati Health for Life program.

EECP does three major things:

1. **It grows new arteries** for anyone suffering from blockages of arteries, anywhere in the body like a natural bypass.

2. **It reverses hardening of the arteries.** EECP promotes secretion of nitric oxide that helps vasodilate and widens arteries to improve circulation and reverse hardening. High blood pressure is stiffness and hardening of the endothelium or artery lining.

3. **It stimulates stem cells** to be released from bone marrow into the circulatory system to repair dysfunctional organs.

The Sara Soulati Health for Life Program

My program is about your lifestyle. With love and support health coaching, we teach you plant-based vegan nutrition. We cut inflammatory foods and eat clean -- fruits, vegetables, grains, nuts, and legumes. We take supplements, work on emotional stress, meditate, walk, exercise, and drink water. We combine our lifestyle coaching with EECP sessions to reverse and prevent cardiovascular disease and a variety of other illnesses.

Our Global Cardio Care® Inc. YouTube https://www.youtube.com/user/globalcardiocare channel has a large library of patient

Sandie West

Creative Chakra Spa

Chakra Energy

Knowledge of the chakra system was discovered thousands of years ago, and has been proven to be nature's apothecary time and time again. In this age of virtual reality, digitization and social media, utilizing the chakra system allows us to turn our focus inward and to block external stimuli that cloud the connection to our mind, body, and spirit. By balancing our internal energy, we are then able to radiate a more positive outward force and strengthen our connection to nature, while offering a more compassionate, open heart toward others.

Importance of Balancing Chakra Energy

Chakras are believed to be centers of the body, spinning and drawing in energy to keep the spiritual, mental, emotional and physical health of the body in balance. They are aligned from the base of the spine to the top of the head and are connected to major organs or glands that govern other body parts. Chakra healing helps clear the pathways so that positive energy can pass through the auric filaments and nurture your physical body.

Indications of Chakra Imbalances

- Overactive 1st Chakra: Paranoia, Aggression, Nervousness, Fear

  Under-active 1st Chakra: Apathy, Weakness, Depression, Passivity, Lethargy

- Overactive 2nd Chakra: Greediness, Addiction, Tension, Compulsivity, Frustration.

  Under-active 2nd Chakra: Disinterest, Repressed Feelings, Self-deprivation, Depression, Sexual Repression.

- Overactive 3rd Chakra: Subjectivity, Bossy, Narrow-Minded, Abrasive

  Under-active 3rd Chakra: Wishy-washiness, Inability to Concentrate, Naive, Passive, Oblivious

- An Open 4th Chakra: Patience, Kindness, Generosity, Peace, Humor, Forgiveness, Love

  Under-active 4th Chakra: Loneliness, Suspicion, Neediness, Possessiveness, Bossiness, Greediness, Jealousy

- Overactive 5th Chakra: Distraction, Negativity, Resentfulness, Preoccupation with Others, Gullibility

  Under-active 5th Chakra: Dishonesty, Willfulness, Hostility, Confusion, Repressed Expression

- Overactive 6th Chakra: Hallucination, Paranoia, Day dreaminess, Tendency to Space out

  Under-active 6th Chakra: Lack of Imagination, Insensitivity, Self-absorption, Narrow-mindedness

- Overactive 7th Chakra: Depression, lack of empathy, confusion, light sensitivity

  Under-active 7th Chakra: Disconnection from reality, frustration, hopelessness, lack of inspiration or joy

It is evident that understanding the chakra system is a simple way to organize your thoughts and beliefs and to empower your life. Compassion for others follows, as you are able to associate the corresponding chakra with a particular behavior. My personal belief is that the Heart Chakra is the most important as it is the center of the chakra system, and energy radiates from this central point. An open heart chakra allows energy to flow more seamlessly to all points in the body.

Creative Chakra Spa

For nearly 2 decades, Creative Chakra Spa has existed as a beach side healing spa retreat, offering 300 holistic products and services. As L.A.'s original destination day spa, it's been featured on America's Next Top Model, MTV, Millionaire Matchmaker, Discovery Channel and E! News.

Our Philosophy

As the founder of Creative Chakra our approach to optimum health is the belief that spas are the hospitals of the future. Eighty percent of disease is caused by stress and the philosophy behind ancient holistic practices such as Ayurveda, yoga, therapeutic massage and facials is to decrease stress levels. These therapies have proven to produce superb and long-lasting effects with regular treatments.

Holistic Aging with a Chakra Natural Lift Facial

The eyes are the window to the soul and a Chakra Lift Facial is one of the best anti-aging treatments that you can give to your skin. It is a natural, holistic approach that helps to attain a younger looking, healthier skin through energy infused techniques using plant enzymes and aromatherapy.

- Rejuvenates and restores a youthful appearance while decreasing the appearance of fine lines & wrinkles

- Tones facial muscles, revives energy and the appearance of your face.

- Capillaries are strengthened, facial lymph is cleansed and skin becomes blemish free

- Reduces puffiness & dark circles, while flushing out potentially harmful toxins by encouraging the flow of oxygen to the tissues

- Release of stress, headaches, PMS symptoms, & relief of sinus congestion. It also reduces puffiness, swelling, and inflammation as well as TMJ.

Creative Chakra Spa is dedicated to holistic health and fitness, empowering and balancing your mind, body, and spirit through chakra energy treatment. The chakras are a window to your soul that ignites feelings of love, power and wellbeing; your spiritual antenna that interprets your inner and outer world.

CPSIA information can be obtained
at www.ICGtesting.com
Printed in the USA
JSHW022125280819
1233JS00003B/20